C000127274

**British Naturalists' Association**

# Guide to
# WILDLIFE
# IN TOWNS

Series Editor   Ron Freethy

**British Naturalists' Association**

# Guide to
# WILDLIFE
# IN TOWNS

## Ron Freethy

**The Crowood Press**

**Cover illustrations**
Top left: Great tit
Top right: Privet hawk moth caterpillar
Bottom left: Cuckoo pint
Bottom right: Fox

First published in 1986 by
THE CROWOOD PRESS
Crowood House,
Ramsbury, Marlborough,
Wiltshire SN8 2HE.

© Ron Freethy 1986

All rights reserved. No part of this publication
may be reproduced or transmitted in any form or
by any means, electronic or mechanical, including
photocopy, recording, or any information storage
and retrieval system, without permission in writing
from The Crowood Press.

**British Library Cataloguing in Publication Data**

Freethy, Ron
 The British Naturalists' Association guide to
 wildlife in towns.—(The British Naturalists'
 Association guides; 5)
 1. Urban fauna — Great Britain
 I. Title    II. Series
 591.52′ 68′ 0941    QH137

 ISBN 0-946284-46-6

Design by Vic Giolitto

Set in 10 on 11 point Bembo by
Quadraset Limited, Midsomer Norton, Bath, Avon

Printed in The Netherlands by Drukkerij Giethoorn/Meppel

# Contents

Foreword 6
Introduction 8
1 Water 13
2 Buildings 32
3 Walls and spaces 48
4 Parks 69
5 Gardens 86
6 Churchyards 106
Further reading 124
Acknowledgements 126
Picture credits 126
Index 127

# Foreword

Since 1905 the British Naturalists' Association has provided opportunities for beginners and more advanced students of natural history to rub shoulders with experts, both amateur and professional.

Throughout this time its magazine, *Country-Side*, and its local, regional and national meetings have fostered the collection and sharing of knowledge concerning the rocks, soils, plants and animals which make up our living landscape. Essential in this process of national learning and the spreading of awareness about wildlife has been the publication of many identification keys – keys to groups like lichens, plant galls, harvestmen and spiders, which though present and often abundant in most habitats were at one time frequently overlooked or wrongly ignored, because there was no way in, no key to unlock the doors of enquiry. In the same way, the Association's pamphlets entitled 'Let's begin the study of . . .' helped pioneer many branches of field science.

At last, some of that knowledge, the fruit of all those eighty years of unique experience, is now made public in this superb series of books. Habitat by habitat, all is revealed.

Most of my own knowledge of plants and animals was gained in the field by walking with and listening to the 'ologists', the experts in each subject – bryology, ornithology, algology etc, etc. Each trip was an occasion to be remembered thanks to the personal anecdotes and sheer enthusiasm of people who had all the facts at their fingertips and who loved the subject of their expertise.

If you can't go on such trips, these books are the next best thing. Open up the pages and you can almost smell the sweet or rotten smell of a river, see the rooks flying from the beech hangers, and hear the warm buzz of summer insects or the crisp crackle of a winter morning.

If I may be allowed one personal reminiscence. I can remember following John Clegg (the author of the volume on ponds and streams in this series) down to the ponds in the grounds of Haslemere Educational Museum, where he was then curator. *Stratiotes aloides* (water soldier), *Nepa cinerea* (the water scorpion), *Hydrocharis morsus ranae* (frogbit), *Gunnera manicata* (the giant prickly rhubarb from South America). . . . This was the first time I was ever shown these things and I will never forget either the experience or the names.

I am grateful to John Clegg and all the others who led me along the many paths of natural history and to a very full and worthwhile life. I am grateful too to all the officers and members of the British Naturalists' Association, both past and present, for everything they have done and are doing to share their knowledge and wonder of life.

What a super series of books! The only problem is what is the B.N.A. going to do to celebrate its centenary?

**David Bellamy**

*President of the Youth Section of*
*the British Naturalists' Association*
Bedburn, County Durham

 **British Naturalists' Association**

The British Naturalists' Association has existed since 1905, when E. Kay Robinson founded the B.N.A.'s journal *Country-Side* and groups of readers began to hold meetings which gave amateur naturalists an opportunity to meet experts and to discuss topics of mutual interest with them. It is this network of branches all over Britain that forms the basis of the B.N.A. New members are always welcome and enquiries regarding membership should be addressed to Mrs June Pearton, 48 Russell Way, Higham Ferrers, Northamptonshire NN9 8EJ.

During its eighty years of existence many distinguished naturalists and public figures have been associated with the B.N.A. At present the President is Lord Skelmersdale, the President of the Youth Section is David Bellamy, and Professor J.L. Cloudsley-Thompson, R.S.R. Fitter, David Hosking, Eric Hosking, Alfred Leutscher, Professor Kenneth Mellanby, Angela Rippon, Sir Peter Scott, Professor Sir Richard Southwood, Sir George Taylor and H.J. Wain are Vice-Presidents of the Association.

*Country-Side* appears four times a year and publishes articles about every aspect of natural history. Contributions, including photographs and drawings, should be addressed to Ron Freethy, The Editor, *Country-Side*, Thorneyholme Hall, Roughlee, Nr Burnley, Lancashire BB12 9LH.

# Introduction

In summer many urban-based naturalists head for the surrounding countryside and leave what they often describe as a lifeless town behind them. In winter many do not stir from the fireside because they believe that most wildlife goes to sleep. They are missing two of nature's most fascinating aspects: the ability of wildlife to thrive in the busiest of towns and its great resistance to the low temperatures of winter.

Because of the often poorly insulated heating systems of houses, shops and factories, the winter temperature in towns is often much higher than in the surrounding rural areas. This welcoming warmth attracts large numbers of birds, especially pigeons, starlings, house sparrows and pied wagtails. In particularly hard weather many other species, including rarities such as waxwings (*Bombycilla garrulus*), are driven into town parks and gardens and are fed by bird-lovers. Many common species are tempted not only to remain throughout the winter but to stay and breed.

Most birds are brought into breeding condition when the increasing hours of spring

**Above** The dry summer of 1984 saw many badgers moving into towns in search of water.

**Below** The fox is becoming increasingly common in city centres.

**Opposite** Hoopoe – occasionally attracted to grassy areas in towns to feed upon insects, especially ants.

Dog rose – a pleasant sight on many urban waste patches.

daylight trigger their reproductive hormones. Street lights burning throughout the dark nights of winter artificially lengthen the hours of light and birds such as the blackbird (*Turdus merula*), robin (*Erithacus rubecula*), dunnock (*Prunella modularis*), mistle thrush (*Turdus viscivorus*) and others always breed earlier in towns than those of the same species which live in the unlit countryside. Research into the relative dates of egg-laying for town and country birds makes an interesting project for naturalists.

It is not only in winter that unusual birds turn up in town centres. During the long hot summer of 1984, in a garden near Southampton I watched a hoopoe (*Upupa epops*) splashing about in an almost dry garden pond after enjoying a meal of ants and bees that it had caught, and a friend photographed a badger (*Meles meles*) trying to obtain a drink from a garden tap near Preston; so birds are not alone in finding urban life to their liking. Every town centre has its shops, cafés and restaurants, and at the end of the day dustbins are full of scraps of food which provide rich pickings for stray cats, dogs, rats, mice and the increasingly common red fox (*Vulpes vulpes*). All a fox requires is a warm place to sleep and a full belly. Drains are easily entered and the warmth of the sewers provides an ideal hide-out after a night visit to the local dustbins. Even in the centre of a busy city, the wildlife is arguably almost as rich as that in the deepest woodland. The animals certainly do not have to work hard for their food once the foxes have removed the lids from the dustbins. The leftovers of the larger mammals are eaten by rodents, which in turn are preyed upon by kestrels (*Falco tinnunculus*), often seen hovering over city centres at first light. I once watched a kestrel kill a mouse while I was waiting for a taxi in the centre of Newcastle-upon-Tyne on a Sunday morning.

The plant life of towns and cities falls into three broad categories. Firstly, there are the wild plants, survivals from the days before the town was built. Odd patches of dog's mercury (*Mercurialis perennis*), cuckoo pint (*Arum maculatum*) with its lovely scarlet berries reflecting the autumn sunlight, ragwort (*Senecio jacobaea*) and groundsel (*Senecio vulgaris*) can still be found in the odd wild corner. Dog rose (*Rosa canina*), dandelion (*Taraxacum officinale*), daisy (*Bellis perennis*), shepherd's purse (*Capsella bursa-pastoris*) and elder (*Sambucus nigra*) add their own splashes of colour. Many of these species, especially the dandelion and shepherd's purse, seem well able to survive being covered by paving stones and road materials and simply grow out through the cracks.

Secondly, there are the plants introduced to town parks and gardens and whose seeds have been spread around the town by wind and animals or by human feet. Many seeds germinate more easily once they have passed through an animal's gut and birds flying over towns may transfer plants from the countryside into towns. Rhododendrons are not slow to spread; fragrant roses and multicoloured primulas often turn up in odd corners even in the busiest towns. Trees such as the sycamore (*Acer pseudoplatanus*) and the London plane (*Platanus* × *hybrida*) have proved particularly resistant to atmospheric pollution and add their graceful beauty to town centres, as well as providing roosts for birds. Because neither

**Above** Woodpigeon – a frequent inhabitant of town parks and gardens.

**Below** Mistle thrush – a species which has learned to use gardens as nest sites.

Cuckoo pint – also known as wild arum and once used as a source of starch for stiffening collars.

of these species is native to Britain they attract fewer insects than the oak or elm, but many species of moth are now showing signs of accepting such newcomers. It is well known that moths are attracted to both street and house lights, and their identification is not so difficult as is often imagined. Town naturalists have a wonderful opportunity here for carrying out original research on moth distribution.

The third class of plants found in towns is those which have been accidentally introduced as a result of industrial processes or human diet. Plants such as teasel (*Dipsacus fullonum*) and soapwort (*Saponaria officinalis*) are still found on river banks in towns, a legacy of old felt works and laundries (*see* Chapter 1). Sewage works are rich in wildlife: decaying matter generates heat and the sludge beds, which never freeze, support vast numbers of invertebrates on which birds of many species feed. The decaying sewage frequently con-

tains exotic seeds which have passed through the human gut. Plants such as melons, peaches and oranges are often found, along with strawberries, potatoes and other fruits and vegetables.

This book will, I hope, amply demonstrate that it is not necessary to leave the boundaries of towns and cities in order to observe wildlife. Indeed, the problems of pollution which not so long ago threatened urban wildlife, although still worrying in many areas, have been reduced significantly now that conservationists and local authorities have begun to work together. A good example of such co-operation was described in an article by David Nicholls in the autumn 1984 newsletter of the Leicestershire and Rutland Trust for Conservation, from which it is clear that Leicester is taking its natural heritage very seriously. This article underlines the part which can be played by amateur naturalists in supporting the work of professionals. Thanks to their combined efforts we may be optimistic that wildlife in towns will fare better in the coming century than it has over the last hundred years.

In these pages the reader will find some uncommon species of plants and animals described, as well as common ones. However, I have not included detailed descriptions of the more well-known birds such as blackbirds, thrushes, starlings, wood pigeons, crows, wrens and tits, since so much has been written about them elsewhere (in field guides, handbooks and bird-table books, for example, some of which are listed in the bibliography). Regarding the less common species of plants, the reader should bear in mind that these are protected by the Wildlife and Countryside Act and it is now illegal to pick, uproot or damage them.

# 1 Water

## Rivers

The health of a city's wildlife can be assessed by monitoring a river flowing through it. When I was a student in London in the late 1950s, the Thames around Cheyne Walk in Chelsea contained few organisms other than species with high loads of haemoglobin, such as the larvae of *Chironomus* midges (known as bloodworms because of their bright red colour) and *Tubifex* worms. These creatures also manage to maintain a tenuous grip on life in the most polluted stretches of the Tyne and Humber. They feed on detritus, including human sewage, and construct tubes in the mud in which they spend most of their lives, projecting their tails, which act as simple gills, out into the water. About this time it became clear that the Thames was something of a human health hazard and that remedial action was essential. This has been startlingly successful, although there are still some blackspots. Fish, including salmon (*Salmo salar*), are now a regular feature of the Thames' fauna. Wildfowl such as tufted duck (*Aythya fuligala*), shelduck (*Tadorna tadorna*), and pochard (*Aythya ferina*) are all regularly seen and the water is much richer in plant and invertebrate life. The only sufferers during this cleaning-up operation have been the gatherers of *Tubifex* worms, who formerly made a splendid living selling the creatures to aquaria shops as food for pet fish.

## Sampling the river's wildlife

City dwellers can use a river as an outdoor aquarium and do a useful job in monitoring its health at the same time. The numbers and species of organisms in the river depend on the level of pollution and so serve as biological in-dicators that highlight heavily polluted areas. Monitoring can be done with a minimum of equipment: a simple net and a white dish is usually all that is needed. With young naturalists, and even with old hands, the dangers of water should be stressed and an area of shallow water chosen. The net is placed close to a stone or other obstruction on its sheltered side so that when the object is lifted the current flushes any organisms hiding beneath it into the net.

Tufted duck (m.) – these ducks are now frequent winter visitors to town ponds.

Shelduck – seen more often in towns in recent years.

In really clean water which is moving fairly rapidly the larvae of both the mayfly and the stonefly are likely to be found. They can be distinguished by the fact that stonefly nymphs have two tails (called *cerci*) whereas mayfly nymphs have three. 'Nymph' is the term used for the young stages of insects that do not have caterpillar and pupa stages as part of their life-cycle. Adult stoneflies and mayflies do not live for very long but their aquatic nymphs spend from one to several years as part of the river fauna, depending on the species. Both are common in fast-running water because they demand high oxygen levels. They are therefore not usually found in urban rivers, since towns and cities are generally sited on the slower stretches, though they may be found beneath weirs, where the water is artificially accelerated and aerated. Thus the fact that stone- and mayflies are absent from a city's river need not be a cause for concern.

## Leeches *Glossiphonia* spp

Leeches provide the best monitor of the beginnings of pollution. Those of the *Glossiphonia* genus are usually found in moderately polluted waters attached by their suckers to stones. The word 'leech' is usually enough to prevent the squeamish from investigating any further for fear of having the blood drained from their bodies. In fact only one of the eleven British species – the medicinal leech (*Hirudo medicinalis*) – can penetrate human skin and it is now very rare in Britain and is, in any case, a creature of still waters. Leeches are related to earthworms and, like earthworms, have segmented bodies. However, they are readily distinguished from worms by the sucker at each end of the body. A few leeches eat small animals whole, but the majority feed by sucking the blood of their hosts, usually fish. Naturalists who dip their nets into reasonably clean town rivers are likely to encounter *Glossiphonia complanata*, which is greenish brown in colour and spotted with yellow and brown around the middle of

 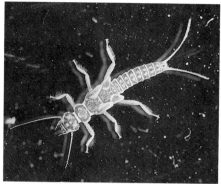

Mayfly larva (**left**) and stonefly larva (**right**) – both these insects occur in unpolluted waters.

the back. Leeches are classified by the number and distribution of the eyes. *G. complanata* has three pairs, although the first pair are usually small and sometimes absent. Since leeches are so elastic it is difficult to describe their length precisely, but normally they are about 3cm (just over 1 inch) long. They are quite sluggish in their movements but quickly roll into a tight ball when touched. Their preferred food is freshwater snails, but when these are scarce – as is often the case since they are very sensitive to pollution – leeches will eat bloodworms instead. This adaptability and the presence of a rich brew of haemoglobin in their own blood enable leeches to survive moderate doses of pollution. As a result, they are common both in stagnant and running water. The smaller *Glossiphonia heteroclita* (1–1·5cm long) is sometimes found in town rivers and is distinguished by its basic colour of clear amber-yellow, with heavy dark spotting on the back.

Horse leech – the most common leech in standing water and canals.

## Freshwater shrimp

*Gammarus pulex*

Perhaps the best pollution indicator is the freshwater shrimp. This creature is easy to identify, since it swims on its side. It is common in fast-moving water but is also found in slower stretches and in still water. It cannot

tolerate heavy pollution. The species offers groups of naturalists an opportunity to conduct a very telling investigation into what happens when water flows into, through and out of a town. Water is sampled in each area, care being taken to net for the same period of time and employ the same method. A large catch of *Gammarus* will be netted above the town, but the catch falls dramatically and often disappears altogether if there is any pollution within the urban environment. When the water improves downstream from the built-up area the numbers rise again. (This is obviously not the case where several heavily

Gammarus – this freshwater shrimp can tolerate only moderate pollution but is active enough to require oxygen.

industrialised towns are dotted along a river and only the one furthest upstream has even moderately pure water.)

*Gammarus* is not a true shrimp, it is an amphipod crustacean – a creature with jointed legs and a body curled when at rest and flattened from side to side. Freshwater shrimps spend most of their time hiding under stones or buried in mud, but they show a surprising turn of speed when disturbed. The male is about 2·5cm (1 inch) long; the female is smaller and is often carried about by the male. She carries her young in a brood patch under the thorax. When they hatch, they look like smaller versions of the parent and grow by a series of moults.

Diet is varied and includes the occasional lapse into cannibalism, but the more usual scavenging habits help *Gammarus* to survive moderate rises in pollution levels. However, the animal's respiratory system prevents it from moving into areas where pollution levels are higher. Raw sewage in particular is a problem since when discharged into a river it is broken down by bacteria, which use up large volumes of oxygen in the process, thus reducing the amount of vital gas available for aquatic wildlife.

This rise in the biological oxygen demand (BOD) spells disaster for active creatures like fish and freshwater shrimps. *Gammarus* has gills at the base of the first four of its thoracic 'legs' and these are kept supplied with fresh water by the beating of the first three pairs of 'legs' on the abdomen. If the creature is observed through a binocular microscope or even a cheap magnifying glass the 'legs' can be seen vibrating furiously to provide oxygenated water for the gills. If the animal is removed from the river current, the vibrations increase visibly. The same effect can be observed when the temperature rises. Many industries discharge hot water directly into a river and, as hot water holds less oxygen than cold, the BOD is automatically affected. This can be clearly demonstrated by adapting the distribution investigation described above and correlating temperatures taken upstream, adjacent to and downstream from a power station, for example, with counts of biological indicator organisms. The situation would be much worse if huge and unsightly cooling towers did not prevent the direct discharge of steam into the river. Other organisms which can be used as indicator species in moderately polluted water are the larvae of blackflies and caddis flies, and the amazing little flatworm *Planaria*.

## Blackflies *Simulium* spp

We could well do without blackflies, since the females enjoy human blood and their bite is quite painful. The eggs are laid in strings on stones close to the water's edge and are gently flushed into the stream by rain. The greyish, cylindrically shaped larvae attach themselves to stones and plants, very often choosing stones in the fastest stretches of the river. These larvae are filter-feeders. A structure around the mouth, which looks and functions like a brush, sweeps small particles – usually unicellular plants – into the mouth. The thoracic region contains a most unusual appendage that looks like a leg but acts as a sucker. There are others on the eighth segment and at the end of the body. These appendages prevent the larva from being swept away by the current which brings it oxygen and food and removes the waste products of its metabolism. The respiratory apparatus is also unusual, taking the form of an extendable gill protruding from the anus. Blackflies can thus exist happily in midstream unless the BOD of the river is so high that the anal gills cannot function.

## Caddis flies

A species of caddis fly, *Hydropsyche*, shares this habitat. It is another filter-feeder and browses on the creatures trapped by a silk net which it spins between stones. Creatures feeding like this are adversely affected by any detergent in the water since, besides being a pollutant in its own right, detergent renders the stones so slippery that attachment is impossible. Caddis flies belong to the insect order Trichoptera. The adults look rather like moths but can be distinguished by their wings, which are hairy (Trichoptera means 'hairy winged') whereas the wings of moths are scaly. The females lay their eggs in clumps usually attached to stones in water and embedded in a jelly that swells rather like frog-spawn. The larvae which hatch from the eggs are purely aquatic. Some caddis flies, like *Hydropsyche*, spin silken webs and are mainly carnivorous. Others are vegetarians. These are much more sluggish and construct cases from dead vegetation, sand grains or stones. The different species can often be identified from the make-up of the cases, but you need to look at them closely, since the occasional larva behaves like a hermit crab and squats in the case of another species.

The majority of caddis larvae live in still waters, but slow flowing river water supports the genus *Limnophilus*, which is made up of many species characterised by their habit of manufacturing heavy cases of plant

Adult caddis fly (*Glyphtaelius pellucidus*).

material, often also incorporating snail shells. The bulk and weight of these cases gives solid protection but restricts movement – though to a vegetarian mobility is not so important. Such species are possibly affected not so much by oxygen shortage caused by pollution as by the shortage of oxygen created by debris in the water. China clay, dust and other materials in suspension prevent light penetrating to the aquatic plants which depend upon it for the process of photosynthesis, in which oxygen is produced as a by-product. In addition to disrupting the river's food chain at its very base, silt also blocks up animals' respiratory organs. Not only is this lethal to fish, but its effect upon invertebrate life is far from minimal.

A variety of caddis cases.

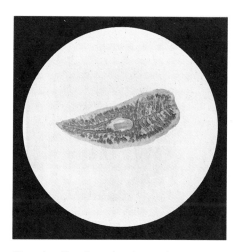

Planarian (*Dendrocoelum lacteum*).

## Flatworms

Perhaps the most bizarre organism found in moderately polluted water is the flatworm *Planaria*, which is common in sluggish streams, attached to the sheltered side of stones. Twelve species occur in Britain. They are free-living freshwater relatives of the liver flukes and tapeworms, with which they make up the unsegmented flatworms called the platyhelminthes. They have flattened bodies, which enables them to squeeze under stones, and are active at night, when they feed greedily on rotting animal matter. It is easy to establish whether you have planarians in the local river by weighting down a small quantity of pet food in a piece of old net. If present, the planarians will scent the meat and come to feed. In times of shortage they are capable of going without food for several weeks, during which period most of the body organs are digested, then reconstituted when better conditions return.

Planarians are the most primitive animals to possess a brain. In the process of research designed to establish whether their memory was electrical or chemical it was found that planarians as small as 1·25cm (½ inch) could be taught to use a maze. Every time the black flatworms turned right they were fed; when they turned left, they were punished by a mild electric shock. Soon all the planarians under test turned right all the time. When the animals were cut into pieces (their power of regeneration is incredible, since each piece builds a new body around itself) the new individuals always turned to the right. Even more bizarre was the fact that when pieces of a trained planarian were fed to an untrained animal the cannibal absorbed the lesson and always turned to the right, never to the left. This research proved conclusively that their memory is chemical.

**Above** Soapwort – its leaves lather and were used in washing.

**Right** Teasel – a useful plant in the old industry of felt making.

## *Tubifex* **and** *Asellus*

As pollution raises the demand for oxygen, the number of species able to survive diminishes. Two particularly resistant common species are the *Tubifex* worm, commonly found in the Thames before the improvement in the quality of its water, and the water louse, *Asellus*, a relative of the woodlouse, which it resembles in its grey-brown colour, its flattened body – about 2·5cm (1 inch) long – and the number and position of its legs. *Asellus* is primarily a scavenger but will also feed on algae, which it scrapes off stones. Counts of *Asellus* along a river indicate with surprising accuracy which are the most heavily polluted areas.

**Opposite** The water hog louse (*Asellus*) is often used as a pollution indicator by biologists.

## Animals of polluted waters

When a sample of river water yields no specimens of *Asellus* it is seriously polluted. Indeed, only special types of organisms can survive in such conditions; and if no animal species is able to live in the moving water, the river is said to be dead. Parts of the Irwell, Mersey, Tyne, Tees and Humber are still in this condition and require urgent – and very expensive – treatment. However, in all large watercourses, especially navigable rivers, there are backwaters where the water is virtually still. Even in heavily polluted backwaters some species are able to survive, such as the larvae of the *Chironomus* midge and of the hoverfly *Eristalis*.

*Chironomus* larvae owe their bright-red colour to the high level of haemoglobin in their blood – essential in order to make the most of the depleted oxygen reserves of the water. They can move by a series of sinuous loops but are usually found conserving their precious oxygen in tubes in the mud. The grey-coloured *Eristalis* does not attempt to extract oxygen from the water itself. It sucks in oxygen directly from the atmosphere by means of a long tube which projects above the water level. The appearance of this tube accounts for the creature's common name of rat-tailed maggot.

## Animals and plants as pollution indicators

It can be seen, therefore, that rivers may be grouped into five categories – clean, moderately polluted, badly polluted and almost or completely dead – and that it is possible for amateur groups or individual naturalists to classify the local water with equipment costing less than £1. A similar technique can be applied to plants, but it does involve the correct identification of algae and the use of a microscope, though useful work can be done with a relatively inexpensive instrument. An additional drawback to the use of algae as pollution indicators is that they are more specifically correlated with sewage pollution and do not therefore give such a clear picture as do the invertebrate animals. The necessary methods are, however, being developed. In 1983 the Nature Conservancy Council produced *Typing British Rivers According to their Flora*, compiled by Dr Nigel Holmes.

Thus the amateur naturalist armed with a microscope and access to a modest library can make an invaluable contribution to the understanding of the wildlife of a city, and schools can ensure that their biological studies are much more useful. One rewarding exercise is to compile a list of plants found growing along the river banks. The Thames is rich in this respect, whilst the heavily polluted northern rivers like the Irwell and the much maligned Mersey each have little oases which blaze with colour and conjure up smells from a bygone age. The Thames, Humber, Tyne, Trent and also the Clyde have similar idyllic areas.

Two plants still found alongside rivers in towns are soapwort and teasel, both of which were at one time cultivated. The scientific name for soapwort is *Saponaria officinalis*. The leaves of this plant, crushed and boiled in water, produce an impressive lather which, in the days when soap was expensive, was used for treating fabric before it was fed into the stamping machines of the mill. The presence of the plant along the tangled vegetation of the river bank, often almost buried beneath heaps of rusting tins, old bedding and confectionery packets, indicates the site of an ancient wash-house or a small mill now lost beneath the maze of warehouses or supermarkets.

Another plant which enables us to read the social history of the city is the teasel. Its scientific name is *Dipsacus fullonum*, but those who used it called it 'clothier's brush', 'brush and comb', 'sweep's brushes' or 'church brooms'. Clothiers used the rough seed heads

of the plant to raise the nap on newly woven cloth. In some parts of the country it is still known as 'Venus's basin', because of the way the leaves clasp the stem and hold water. Flies drown in these basins and their decaying bodies are absorbed by the plant, which is therefore partly insectivorous.

A fascinating project for the city dweller is to wander along the river banks making a list of the plants found – there will be more than you would expect – then look up their ancient uses. Dandelions, for example, were once cultivated for salads and also for latex, which was used as a glue. Daisies were used to make eye-ointment, mugwort to flavour ale and willow to cure headaches (the bark contains aspirin). The list is endless. Plantain and pineapple weed, coltsfoot, cuckoo pint and creeping buttercup, ragwort, rosebay willowherb, rushes and mint can all be found with a little diligent hunting – and with some enjoyable

Pied wagtail.

detective work the history of the riverside can be unravelled.

## Birds of the river

Birds to be found by the river include the resourceful pied wagtail and scavenging gulls, particularly black-headed and herring gulls. Wrens and robins sing from the remnants of woodlands that still survive on the odd corner where the river meander has not yet been 'managed'. I was once drinking a quiet pint of beer on the terrace of a Thames-side pub when I noticed a pied wagtail feeding from a plastic tray which had held someone's fish-and-chip lunch. As usual, the river had been used as a dumping ground and the tray had floated downstream and lodged with other debris in the trailing branches of an alder on a bend of the river. I was reminded of the old country

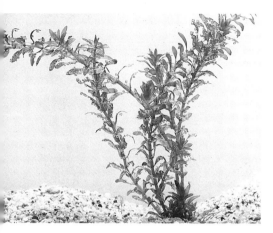

Canadian pondweed can be a menace in ponds and canals.

name for this spruce little bird, 'washerwoman'. This had its origins in the days when the villagers, still dressed in their best clothes, washed their Sunday dishes in the stream, usually in the company of this 18cm (7 inch) black and white little dandy with its flicking tail. The village may have become first a town then a city, but people still use the river as a dumping ground and scraps are plentiful, whilst a ruined warehouse, crumbling wall, overhanging bramble or the hulk of a barge afford a wide choice of nesting sites.

## Canals

In many cities the existing river proved inadequate for the needs of industry and canals were cut. However well these are constructed – and some are masterpieces of engineering – they lose some water by seepage, a lot by evaporation and some by deliberate extraction. These losses have to be made up from large compensation reservoirs and, whilst the canals must have caused great disruption during construction, on balance they have proved to be a boon for wildlife.

## Canadian pondweed *Elodea canadensis*

Canadian pondweed was introduced from North America into a small tributary of the river Cam in 1848 and multiplied vegetatively to such an extent that it was a hazard to river traffic by 1880 and has since spread from river to river via drainage ditches and canals. Male specimens are very rare, but the female plant has very brittle stems as well as a phenomenally quick growth rate, and the spread is assisted by boats which grind up the weed. It overwinters as tightly wrapped leaves, which await the return of warm weather before growing rapidly once more. The initial vigorous spread has slowed in recent years and, unless regular reproduction by sexual means becomes a feature, it may well lack the genetic variations essential for survival over a long period.

Canal locks are excellent places for the botanist to go hunting. The sluices simulate stretches of fast water and here may be found long-leaved water crowfoot, on which feast several species of freshwater snail – which in turn makes the area popular with moorhens. Lock gates and bridges provide a congenial habitat for plants such as skullcap (*Scutellaria galericulata*), gypsywort (*Lycopus europeaus*) and butterbur (*Petasites hybridus*). In the days when the canals provided a direct link between the farms and cotton fields of America and the inland towns of Britain cargoes often accidentally brought alien species into our midst, and it is worthwhile looking for such introductions close to old warehouses or areas where cargo was unloaded. Many areas of canal have stands of the monkey flower (*Mimulus guttatus*) and pineapple weed (*Matricaria matricarioides*) which may well have spread by this method. Himalayan balsam (*Impatiens glandulifera*) is another interesting plant whose spread has been assisted by the inland waterways system. It has proved to be surprisingly resistant to pollution.

# Wildfowl

Canal reservoirs vividly underline the fact that not all human activities are detrimental to wildlife. The reservoirs act as roosting sites for wildfowl, which frequently spend the day feeding on rivers, including the London Thames and parts of the Nottingham Trent. Before the improvement in the quality of the water such movements were impossible. Wildfowl counts are highest in winter and many naturalists' groups keep regular records so they know when each species reaches its peak population. Such information can help to save birds in the event of an oil spill in a river since it is vital to know which species are likely to be affected, where they spend their

**Right** Butterbur – a member of the dandelion family which grows in wet places.

**Below** Teal love to hide among vegetation and are often overlooked around town ponds.

time and how many are likely to be in an area on a particular date. Wildfowl species occurring on rivers in towns are the mute swan (*Cygnus olor*), shelduck (*Tadorna tadorna*), teal (*Anas crecca*), pochard (*Aythya ferina*), tufted duck (*Aythya fuligula*) and wigeon (*Anas penelope*). I have recorded all of these species on the Thames, as well as on the Mersey opposite Liverpool's Liver Building. I have also noted tufted duck, mallard (*Anas platyrhynchos*) and even goldeneye (*Bucephala clangula*) on the Irwell, close to the centre of Manchester, despite the filth of the river in this area. The river Severn near Bristol and the Humber close to Hull are other areas where wildlife is fighting back.

The mute swan populations have been giving cause for concern in recent years and in 1979 the situation on rivers in the Midlands was so bad that the Nature Conservancy Council was asked to survey the population. In 1981 their report 'Lead Poisoning in Swans' was produced. Swans are mainly vegetarian and have been estimated to consume about 4kg (9lb) of wet plants per day. They obtain these by up-ending and stretching their necks to reach the bottom. The occasional invertebrate animal is ingested along with an appreciable amount of grit. When feeding on the coastal marshes swans may pick up lead pellets from the spent cartridges of wildfowlers. In city centres and parks the main problem is the shot discarded by the increasing numbers of anglers. The sight of a swan dying of lead poisoning would appal them. The proud posture of the neck is abandoned, eyes glaze over and blood vessels rupture. Death comes slowly. Substitutes for lead shot have recently been introduced but are only slowly gaining acceptance among conservative anglers. The problem would be minimised if anglers took particular care not to spill their shot and not to discard it after use.

Lead poisoning is not the only danger faced by swans in urban situations. Many casualties occur when swans fly into overhead power cables. In many areas securing large corks to the power lines has made them easier to see and has cut down collisions. This is yet

| Causes of death in Mute Swans: results of post-mortem examinations 1980-81 | | | | | | | | | | | |
|---|---|---|---|---|---|---|---|---|---|---|---|
| | Thames | Trent | Avon | Norfolk/Suffolk | Midlands | Southern England | Northern England | Wales | Scotland | All examinations | % for England | % of total |
| Lead poisoning | 43 | 12 | 7 | 17 | 11 | 3 | 12 | 8 | 0 | 113 | 50.0 | 39.2 |
| Collisions | 5 | 3 | 1 | 7 | 9 | 5 | 0 | 0 | 49 | 79 | 14·2 | 27·4 |
| Internal injuries | 5 | 0 | 2 | 6 | 5 | 4 | 1 | 0 | 6 | 29 | 10·9 | 10.0 |
| Infection, parasitism, etc. | 2 | 2 | 0 | 8 | 6 | 3 | 2 | 2 | 5 | 30 | 10·9 | 10.4 |
| Shot or killed | 1 | 0 | 0 | 0 | 8 | 1 | 0 | 0 | 6 | 16 | 4·76 | 5·5 |
| Oiled | 0 | 0 | 0 | 0 | 2 | 0 | 0 | 0 | 0 | 2 | 0·9 | 0·6 |
| No diagnosis | 9 | 1 | 0 | 5 | 0 | 2 | 0 | 1 | 1 | 19 | 8·0 | 6·6 |

Total number of birds examined 288

another field where naturalists' groups can make a positive contribution. Regular counts of birds should be made and areas close to power lines searched, which can easily be done from a distance using binoculars. Areas of particular danger will soon become obvious and a letter to the local electricity board usually receives a constructive response. Oil spills are another problem and naturalists spotting a potential danger should notify The British Trust for Ornithology. Interference by vandals in breeding activities constitutes another serious threat to swan populations.

A Nature Conservancy Council report published in 1980 investigated the cause of death of 288 swans. The table shows the situation clearly. London swans are particularly vulnerable to lead poisoning – a hazard almost unknown in Scotland, where fly fishing pre-

Mute swan – lead shot has caused an alarming decline.

dominates. There, power lines are a more frequent threat. One naturalists' group near Manchester regularly surveys the local rivers, canals and associated reservoirs. Although they often record nil returns, an increase in numbers is already being detected as pollution on the rivers is slowly but surely reduced. The Manchester Ship Canal, not so many years ago one of the busiest inland waterways in the world, now carries fewer than two large ships a day into Manchester and is threatened with closure. The birds, including swans, are poised ready to take over, and five times in 1983 a kingfisher (*Alcedo atthis*) was sighted on the canal less than a mile from Manchester docks.

The study of birds in cities is not only

**Above** As pollution levels fall many kingfishers are returning to urban riversides.

**Below** Great crested grebe – a species which has found gravel pits very much to its liking.

enjoyable but essential from the point of view of conservation. During the preparation of this chapter I spent some time birdwatching on the Thames and on the rivers Bollin and Irwell, both tributaries of the Mersey close to the city of Manchester. Just upstream from Putney Bridge on the Thames are the Barn Elms reservoirs, which always carry an impressive number of wildfowl as well as an often huge roost of gulls. Many other areas of the Thames, including Battersea and the Surrey Docks, are now undergoing a face-lift, with naturalists well to the fore in the operations. The river is used by visiting birds as a flight path. Birds on migration can fly above 10,000 feet; as I watched a flight of pochard drop into Barn Elms, a jumbo jet on its way to Heathrow roared overhead. This is one reason why we need to know all we can about birds in cities. Pollution was already with us when aircraft were invented and as the environment improves, the rising bird population will bring an increased risk of airstrikes. Ornithologists must know where the birds are, when they migrate and at what height, and the precise time of year when migrations occur. Radar can help provide this information, but the records of local naturalists collected over a long period are likely to be just as valuable. Similarly, as the Mersey is cleaned up, a process which it is estimated will take at least twenty-five years, the bird population will rise and Manchester's Ringway and Liverpool's Speke airports will need to take extra precautions against airstrikes. The cities of the Midlands, especially Birmingham and Nottingham, as well as Glasgow and Edinburgh would also find a knowledge of bird movements close to their airports most valuable.

The demands of urban life have produced not only artificial waterways in the form of canals and reservoirs, but two other aquatic habitats which have been and are still being created close to city centres. These are gravel pits and park lakes.

# Gravel pits

The construction of new roads demands gravel, and its extraction leaves an unsightly hole in the ground, as does subsidence in mining areas. In the past gravel pits would have been left as gaping holes, but they are now often allowed to flood and are planted with native trees such as willow, alder, hawthorn and ash. Other seeds are carried in by birds and a thriving nature reserve soon develops. Two pleasing examples are the Chorlton and Sale Water Parks close to Manchester, just off the M63 motorway, both only recently constructed. Already the winter wildfowl counts are high, including the occasional bittern and water-rail, and in summer moorhen, coot, mallard and both sedge and reed warblers breed in these parks, whilst grebes display happily, exchanging gifts of waterweed and chasing each other across a stretch of clear water which only three years ago was an ugly scar in the ground. Both parks are open to and used by the public, but care has been taken to leave a place for birds.

A similar project which has already proved successful is at Ruxley Gravel Pits, Orpington, only about twelve miles from the centre of London, just off the Sidcup bypass. The reserve is run by the Kent Trust for Nature Conservation in partnership with the Orpington and District Angling Association and the Southern Water Authority. A permit is needed to visit and I must confess that I wondered how the area could be designated a Site of Special Scientific Interest (SSSI) with traffic roaring almost ceaselessly along the bypass. A visit to the pits, from which gravel was extracted from 1929 to 1951, soon convinced me. I counted over twenty great crested grebes displaying, a kingfisher flashed across a belt of bulrushes, and siskins and long-tailed tits could be seen feeding on the seeds of alder. Flocks of teal, splendidly neat tufted ducks and a preening group of pochards, their red heads gleaming in the

Water vole – a shy member of the waterside community.

sunlight, proved that given half a chance there is nothing so resilient as wildlife. Mammals are also present, including water voles (*Arvicola terrestris*) and field voles (*Microtus agrestis*), as well as the engaging little harvest mouse (*Micromys minutus*), Britain's smallest mammal.

## Great crested grebe *Podiceps cristatus*

Of all the species that have benefited from such schemes the great crested grebe must have gained the most. There is no doubt that this bird's attractive plumage almost caused its extinction as the millinery trade strived to design more and more bizarre hats, without any thought for conservation. A series of Bird Protection Acts in 1870, 1873, 1877 and 1953 improved the desperate situation. At the turn of the century the population numbered fewer than 100 pairs, but since 1931 the population has been regularly monitored and from just over 1,000 pairs in the 1930s the population has now risen to over 5,000 pairs. While gravel pits are sometimes disturbed by anglers, they are usually less suitable for water sports than reservoirs, which offer larger and more open stretches of water.

The great crested grebe is the largest European grebe, being about 48cm (19 inches) long. The sexes cannot be distinguished, and both male and female are typified by a black crest and delightful breeding frills around the neck. These are fringed with soft chestnut and look like an Elizabethan ruff, especially when spread during display. After a most exciting display chase over the water, the pair exchange waterweed in a sort of mating ceremony before building a nest from a pile of vegetation. From three to six chalky-white

Common frog.

eggs are laid and are incubated by both parents for about a month. The young are striped and look most attractive as they hitch a lift on their parents' backs, tucking themselves in amongst the feathers. The main item in the diet of grebes is fish, but frogs, especially during the tadpole stage, are also eaten eagerly.

## Common frog *Rana temporaria*

The frog has had something of a lean time recently and far from being common it is now absent from many parts of Britain as a result of pollution, extensive loss of habitat caused by drainage schemes and overcollecting by schools and universities. Mercifully this latter practice is now much less widespread and, thanks to a more positive approach to conservation, there are signs that some city habitats, including gravel pits and even small gardens, are now meeting the needs of this animal. A positive step would be to set aside part of each park lake, preferably on one of the islands, as a marshy area and, if necessary, to introduce frogs onto it. Some adults and tadpoles would undoubtedly be eaten by grebes and especially by wildfowl such as tufted ducks, whilst herons (*Ardea cinerea*) would also take their share, but with patience the return of frogs to towns could be ensured and each square metre of marshland created should be welcomed, since no waterside habitat has suffered more from the development of cities along the flood plains of rivers.

## Walthamstow Marshes

London, for example, has lost all of its natural marshland except at Walthamstow. How heartening it was, therefore, to see the success of the 'save the marshes' campaign in the early 1980s which ensured that the city's last link with its primeval marshland was not severed.

A heron on its way into town in search of food.

The group left nothing to chance and conducted a thorough survey of the wildlife. This not only saved the marsh but clearly showed how many varieties of fauna and flora can exist within the confines of the busiest of cities. Between 1974 and 1979 Graham Brandjes recorded some 126 species of bird, including such rarities as the black-throated diver (*Gavia arctica*), great northern diver (*Gavia immer*), red-necked grebe (*Podiceps griseigena*), bittern (*Botaurus stellaris*), white stork (*Ciconia ciconia*), ruddy duck (*Oxyura jamaicensis*), osprey (*Pondion haliaetus*), pectoral sandpiper (*Calidris melanotos*), glaucous gull (*Larus hyperboreus*) and bearded tit (*Panurus biarmicus*). The plant life also proved to be prolific and about 350 species

were recorded, belonging to over 60 botanical families. This base means that there is ample food for insects and seventeen breeding species of butterflies were discovered, including the Essex skipper (*Thymelicus lineola*), which is declining over most of its habitat but is increasing at Walthamstow. The larvae feed on such grasses as couch, timothy and catstail, all of which are abundant on the site. The marshes tell another success story, regarding Roesels' bush cricket (*Metrioptera roeselii*). The campaign booklet noted that the species 'is quite restricted in this country, mainly to southern Kent, northern and central Norfolk, southern Hampshire and the Isle of Wight. The Roesels' song is truly beautiful.'

Walthamstow Marshes illustrate why such areas should be left alone and the recent decline in dockland areas has, similarly, given nature a chance to show just how resilient it is.

Naturalists' groups have been making observations of these areas for many years and their records are vital to our understanding of the natural history of towns. Alex Clarke published the following note in *Country-Side* in autumn 1983, which underlines how important such work can be:

## An unusual form of goat's rue
*(Galega officinalis)* (L)

On Saturday 3 July 1982 I conducted a party from my Epping Forest branch of the British Naturalists' Association around the now disused Royal Group of Docks situated in the East End of London. Having made a study of the flora and fauna of this area for twenty-five years, this ramble was always popular with our members, as anything was likely to be found.

Whilst studying botany in the now filled-in section of the Old Barge Lock situated at the western entrance of the Royal Victoria Dock, a very large individual of an extremely odd plant was found. The plant had inconspicuous green flowers growing in a spiral up the stem. No one present was able to identify the mysterious find.

A small specimen was taken by one of our members, Barbara Holmes, to the British Natural History Museum at Kensington for identification. Our find aroused considerable interest amongst the staff there. I was put in contact with a Mr Michael Mullin from the British Museum and was able to take him to the site on 15 July. After various deliberations and taking of photographs he decided that it was a sport of *Galega officinalis* (L) which grew all around it. Later he confirmed to me that this form was very unusual and previously unrecorded in Great Britain. As I understand it, this monstrosity is in teratological form, where all the petals and flower parts have been changed into bracts and bracteoles. This is usually due to some special environmental factor affecting the offspring of a plant.

On the last Saturday in November 1982 I was invited by Mr Mullin to the annual exhibition of the Botanical Society of the British Isles at the British Museum of Natural History. On show was our British Naturalists' Association (Epping Forest Branch) 'first', with his report, and beside it the usual form of *Galega officinalis* for comparison.

# 2 Buildings

A stroll around the dockland area of a city early in the morning provides ample evidence of the presence of the brown rat; and if permission is obtained to enter a warehouse, the beam of your torch will quickly reveal many more brown rats and the occasional black rat scurrying about the warehouse floor. No account of urban wildlife would be complete without some mention of these maligned creatures. Both were accidentally introduced by man's commercial enterprises and, as is so often the case, found a niche not being utilised by any native species. The brown rat now seems to be ousting its less competitive black cousin, which arrived in Britain first. In their native lands these rodents had been controlled by predators, but in their new habitat their traditional predators were absent and the rat population expanded quickly. Even the constraint of a limited food supply does not apply in warehouses full of food-stuffs and the range of food items acceptable to a rat is quite staggering. This is also true of the house mouse, another rodent introduced from abroad, but some degree of control is exercised both by domestic cats and by cats which live ferally in towns and by the kestrel, which has also adapted well to urban life. Studies of these five species, often undertaken by amateurs, have shown how perfectly each fits into its ecological niche.

## Rats and mice

### Black rat *Rattus rattus*

Perhaps better referred to as the ship rat, the black rat almost certainly evolved in southeastern Asia and spread rapidly around the world via the ancient trade routes. In countries with cooler climates its spread was slower. Because of its habit of running around the rafters, the black rat is also sometimes called the 'roof rat'. Its presence in a building can be confirmed by dirty smears on walls caused by the passage of the animal's wet body. These smears differ from those of the brown rat by being deposited in a series of discontinuous loops rather than the unbroken pattern typical of *Rattus norvegicus*.

The black rat probably reached Britain in the eleventh century and accidental introductions continued throughout the Crusades. Its population has declined steadily in recent years, possibly because of its failure to compete with the brown rat but more probably because it restricts itself to living in buildings, where it has proved easier to eradicate. Nowadays its presence is largely confined to seaports.

If you look at a black rat closely, you will see that the fur is shiny black on the dorsal surface, while the belly is creamy white. It is, in fact, quite a handsome animal and it is hardly surprising that the pelt once brought a good price in the market-place.

In common with other rodents, including the brown rat, the black rat support fleas that feed on human blood. For this reason it was the main agency by which the Black Death virus spread so rapidly and became the scourge of the Middle Ages. It has also been found capable of spreading typhus, and so on hygienic grounds its presence cannot be tolerated in any numbers. In economic terms the black rat also poses a threat to human commerce, since it is more of a vegetarian than the brown rat and can devastate stores of commodities such as cocoa, sugar and cereals.

Black rat.

*The Handbook of British Mammals* mentions that it is even fond of chilli peppers.

## Brown rat *Rattus norvegicus*

The brown rat has several other common names, including common, Norway, sewer and Hanoverian rat. The last owes its origin to the arrival of the species in Britain at the same time as the Hanoverian monarchs, who were equally unpopular. The species spread immediately and buildings were soon being fouled by its droppings. These are about 12mm (½ inch) long and pointed at both ends. They are deposited in groups, in contrast to those of the black rat, which are deposited singly and have blunt ends.

The brown rat's range of diet and habitat are so wide that its success was assured. In addition to materials which we would consider edible, rats have been known to eat lead water-pipes, electric cables and building timbers – and burst pipes and warehouse fires are frequently caused by their open-rooted incisors, which do not wear out but continue growing throughout the life of the animal.

In recent years pest control officers have been alarmed to find that so-called 'super-rats' are now able to eat and digest the rat poison Warfarin without any apparent ill effects. A persistent effort is needed merely to hold the numbers of urban rats steady; to eradicate them would appear at the present time to be

**Above** Brown rat eating ice.

**Below** House mice will even eat old rope.

Cats are one of the chief enemies of town birds.

completely beyond us. This is particularly true in places such as rubbish dumps, sewers and polluted rivers. Unlike the black rat, the brown rat thrives in and around rivers. I once watched a rat on the River Irwell in Manchester sitting by a frozen sewage inlet eating ice with what seemed obvious enjoyment, as the crunching sound of its teeth sliced through the early morning air.

Another important reason for the success of the brown rat is its efficient breeding cycle. Providing enough food is available, breeding continues throughout the year and up to five litters may be produced annually. Gestation takes just over three weeks, the young being born naked and blind; within three weeks the young are weaned and a female brown rat is able to conceive when she is only three months old.

## House mouse *Mus musculus*

Naturalists in urban situations can learn the techniques of estimating animal populations by working on house mouse populations. The method used is a technique of trapping and retrapping in which the animals caught are not killed. This humane treatment of a pest goes against the grain with some people, but it is only when we understand the life history of a creature that we stand any chance of being able to control it. Live traps for small mammals, such as the Longworth trap, are on sale and are easy to use and to transport, though rather expensive. Pitfall traps can be made easily from large jars baited with food, set flush with the animal's run. Once a mouse or other small mammal has fallen into the trap, it cannot climb the smooth sides to get out. It is then marked, either with paint or by clipping a toe nail, and released. The traps are now re-set and some of the animals caught previously will be captured again, along with others not previously trapped. The total population can then be estimated by the formula:

$$\text{total population} = \frac{\text{no caught in sample 1} \times \text{no caught sample 2}}{\text{no of marked animals recaptured}}$$

Care is needed in setting the traps, but with practice the technique can be mastered and the population assessed with some confidence.

The name 'house mouse' seems too restrictive for a species which has been found down mines, up hills, in heated warehouses and even in deep-freezes. It may well have been with us since we lived in caves, and archaeological evidence shows that mice were certainly present in Iron Age Britain. Breeding continues throughout the year and with a gestation period of nineteen days as many as ten litters can be produced in a year, with up to eight young born at a time. Small wonder that *Mus musculus* is impossible to eradicate – despite poisons, traps and cats.

## Feral cats

Domestic cats can make hunting trips from their home base, but many live permanently in the open and these so-called feral cats are particularly efficient hunters.

The only thing certain about the origin of domestic cats is that they have existed since the earliest times. Indeed, in ancient Egypt cats played a prominent role in mythology and religion and were often mummified. Until recently it was suggested that there were two possible species from which the domestic cat might have evolved. These were the European wild cat (*Felis sylvestris*) and the African wild cat (*Felis lybyca*). However, taxonomists have now demonstrated that the two are really part of a single species, showing a gradual variation over the whole range.

Cats are generally more independent than dogs by nature and a number have always chosen to live on their own, quite independent of man. This, then, is the origin of the feral cat, which is quite distinct from the wild cat. They are, however, still given the same scientific name as they are inter-fertile. Feral cats are also common in the countryside as well as in the centre of towns. Detailed study of these cats has long been neglected, but some progress was made by Roger Tabor, one-time editor of the journal of the British Naturalists' Association. His book *The Wildlife of the Domestic Cat*, published in 1983, is based on his observation of a colony of feral cats in London's Fitzroy Square. Tabor postulated that the 'blotched tabby', so loved in Britain today, arrived in many dockland cities throughout the world from the time of Elizabeth I onwards as ships' cats deserted. The Fitzroy Square cats, however, seem to be of Phoenician origin and are mainly black with white socks and bib. Tabor's book focused the urban naturalist's attention on the feral cat, which has been increasingly threatened by people with no knowledge about it but with a fixed prejudice against it. Are cats that live rough in towns a threat to our health? Or should we welcome them and leave them alone because they remove rodent pests? In May 1984 the BBC transmitted a film made by London Scientific Films. In a preview in the *Radio Times* Frances Donnelly described a problem faced by the cameraman, Jim Black:

But what Jim Black very quickly found was that finding a colony of feral cats to examine was going to be extremely difficult, due to the attentions of various cat pressure groups. The Fitzroy colony had been trapped and neutered shortly after Roger's book was published, and the cats were no longer in any sense 'wild' since neutered cats tend to sit around looking glum. Furthermore, most of the major colonies had been dealt with. Jim Black saw that the real question was what's happening to the feral cat in London, and is it fair?

Feral cats are under attack from a number

of groups, some activated by caring interests, some by commercial interests who simply see them as another pest like cockroaches, and want them exterminated. In the film we see a colony of feral cats in North London before, during and after the attentions of Melvyn the pest-control man, who specialises in cats and tries to make the process as humane as possible. After his visit, of the thirty-four cats that are trapped fifteen go to a cat sanctuary, six are returned to the site minus some vital equipment, twelve are gassed and one very young kitten is 're-housed'. But being put in a cat sanctuary usually means a humane death at a later date; the chances of anyone wanting to adopt an adult, traumatised wild cat are slim. In the film we see the big black tom, the leader of the community, being neutered and returned to the site. He was one of the lucky ones.

Besides the pest-control men, feral colonies are also under constant scrutiny from animal welfare groups who also believe that there are too many feral cats, and lobby local authorities to provide funds to enable them to control the local cat population in their area. Groups such as SNIP – the 'Society for the Neutering of Islington's Pussies' – have gained the council's support for the wholesale neutering of local cats. There's also widespread support for a nationwide neutering of feral cats.

'What worries me', says Jim Black, 'is that there's a great deal of activity going on to control the numbers of feral cats, but when we challenged these pressure groups to produce evidence that there was a problem, no one was able to show us any conclusive or reliable figures. We know that there are more feral cats in London nowadays largely as a result of the war, when many cats became homeless and found they could live perfectly well without human intervention.'

'But this still doesn't mean there is necessarily a problem,' he adds, 'which is the way it's being treated.'

The resulting film, showing in an unbiased way what is actually happening to London's feral cats, is bound to distress a lot of animal lovers. London Scientific Films have unflinchingly filmed cats being trapped, chloroformed and castrated in graphic detail.

Part of the visual shock of this comes from the fact you may very well be watching the television with your own cat purring contentedly on your knee as you see its cousin on the screen looking hunted, terrified and bloody. Cats arouse strong and peculiar emotions in human beings, as the poems of T. S. Eliot attest. The black-and-white cats of Fitzroy Square were nicknamed 'Jellicle cats' after the cat of that name in T. S. Eliot's poem, the black-and-white 'clubland' cat who goes out at night in white spats and full evening dress.

In fact, in summing up this whole muddled and emotional issue one might easily fall back on T. S. Eliot's famous dictum after studying the text of Hamlet, when he remarked that the play had clearly mattered to Shakespeare in a way that we couldn't understand, that the emotion displayed in it was 'far in excess of the actual plot'.

The emotion experienced towards feral cats also seems much in excess of what the issue is actually about: there seems to be a number of passionately committed people extremely active about a problem that no one has actually proved is a problem. We seem unable to leave feral cats alone; we seem to need to intervene in their lives.

'And yet somehow you're left with the feeling that, in spite of all this well-meaning activity, the cats aren't getting a fair deal,' says Jim Black. 'Are the only options really to kill, neuter or incarcerate them? Isn't there another alternative: simply leaving them alone?'

Kestrel with a field vole – both common in towns.

All naturalists must applaud this sentiment – after all, cats do not transmit disease and many are friendly to human intruders into their territory, especially if they are used to being fed. What is needed is a co-ordinated in-depth study of the urban cat, perhaps coupled with a 'trap and retrap' programme to calculate their population, as well as a study of their diet. These, I am sure, would show that the feral cat is providing a valuable service by exercising some control on the rodent populations.

## Birds

### Kestrel *Falco tinnunculus*

Every animal has two basic needs – adequate food and a safe breeding site. In woodland a kestrel requires a supply of small rodents, usually short-tailed field voles, plus the occasional small bird, and the old nest of a crow or perhaps a hollow tree in which to in-cubate its eggs and raise its young. A city blasted by war or undergoing a redevelopment programme has open areas of rubble in which rodents such as rats and mice abound, and the kestrel's hovering flight enables it to keep station over a potentially rich feeding area. The large populations of house sparrows and starlings so typical of city buildings provide variety of diet. Window-ledges offer perfect nest sites and kestrels have proved not too particular in their choice of lodgings. In London a warehouse in the Surrey Docks, the House of Lords, a ledge on a bridge near Waterloo Station and the Savoy Hotel have all been employed as nesting sites since breeding was first recorded as long ago as 1931. The city centres of Birmingham, Nottingham, Glasgow, Edinburgh and Bristol all have resident kestrels.

Very rare mutant blue/white blackbird.

## Bird pellets

The diet of the kestrel can be studied by examining the pellets which it coughs up after feeding and which with careful searching can be found on the ground below kestrel nest sites, since they double as feeding stations. It is usually suggested that birds of prey swallow their prey whole and eject the parts such as feathers and bones that cannot be digested. However, this description is slightly misleading, since it is not only owls and other birds of prey that produce pellets. In fact, most, if not all, birds do so – including starlings, dunnocks, robins and crows – and gulls drop a litter of pellets below their night roosts around urban reservoirs. It should also be pointed out that diurnal birds of prey have very powerful digestive juices, which can occasionally even break down skeletal tissue. As a result, the pellets of owls, which have weaker digestive juices, often have more in them than those of hawks and falcons.

Urban naturalists can do much valuable work by collecting and analysing bird pellets. In order to analyse the pellets they should first be soaked in a saucer of warm water, perhaps with a drop of disinfectant added, then teased apart with mounted needles and the prey items lifted out either with forceps or, if they are very delicate, with a small paintbrush. Mounted needles do not necessarily have to be purchased but can be made from darning needles and corks, or tweezers can be used instead. The bones and skulls of mammals (which are solid), the wing cases of beetles and the feathers and skulls of birds are always fairly obvious; since bird bones are lighter and are hollow, they are more easily crushed than those of mammals and are therefore generally more difficult to identify. However, there are leaflets and books on the market which can help a great deal. Particularly useful is the four-page booklet *Collecting and Analysing*

*Bird Pellets* by David Glue available from the Royal Society for the Protection of Birds, which first appeared in *Bird Life*, the RSPB's magazine for young ornithologists.

A valuable research programme can also be carried out on the pellets of smaller birds. Blackbirds, for example, seem to prefer to eat large, juicy common earthworms (*Lumbricus terrestris*) and to avoid brandlings (*Eisenia foetida*). Positive proof of deliberate selection by blackbirds and other birds could be obtained by analysis of their pellets, since the setae – the bristles by which earthworms move themselves – are indigestible and the shape of the setae varies according to species.

## House sparrow *Passer domesticus*

House sparrows are found wherever man has made his home, with the exception of a few remote mountain farmhouses and the occasional offshore island. Birds of both sexes are about 14cm (5¾ inches) long and can be distinguished easily. The cock has a grey crown with a pale chestnut border at the back and sides, and a black bib which can be seen at all seasons although it is much more prominent in the breeding period. The back is a rich streaked brown, which contrasts with the paler underparts, and there is a distinct bar on the brown wing – a feature present but much less prominent in the female. The hen and young are dull brown above and dingy white beneath, but what they lack in colour is more than compensated for by their strength of character.

House sparrows often breed in colonies, building their untidy straw nests lined with feathers in holes under the eaves of buildings, which provides a warmer and much drier habitat than they could expect to find in the wild. When cities depended on horses for transport straw was a plentiful nesting material and flies and beetles in the dung provided food for the young. Always resourceful, sparrows have been known to use strips of newspaper, crisp packets and paper handker-

chiefs to make a cosy cradle in which between three and six eggs are laid. The eggs are coloured greyish-white with dark blotches and are incubated by the female alone for about fifteen days. The male then helps to feed the young for a further period of fifteen days until they fledge.

The choice of food shows just how versatile sparrows are. I have watched them feed their young high on a ledge at Waterloo Station with the remains of a British Rail sandwich. On another occasion, I witnessed a pair of sparrows in Covent Garden catching flies apparently drunk from feeding on rotting and fermenting fruit waiting to be collected by the dustmen. The short breeding cycle gives sufficient time for three broods to be raised in a season – though the breeding season is hard to define, since eggs may be incubated in every month of the year. House sparrows are especially difficult to census because of their habit, unique in British birds at least, of using their own nests as winter roosts and for protection against predators such as the kestrel. They are, therefore, quite likely to pair off and remain in a territory throughout their lives.

## Urban variations

When watching common birds such as house sparrows it quickly becomes apparent how much variation there is within the population, especially with regard to the presence of albino or partially albino birds. Albinism seems to be especially frequent in urban blackbirds. It has been suggested that it is caused by the unnatural, vitamin-deficient diet of birds in towns, but I strongly suspect it may also have something to do with the fact that there is less of a struggle to survive in towns and colour aberrants are more likely to survive. This includes other colour variations as well as albinism.

In recent years there have also been an increasing number of sightings of birds, often house sparrows but sometimes starlings, with unusually shaped bills which would not allow

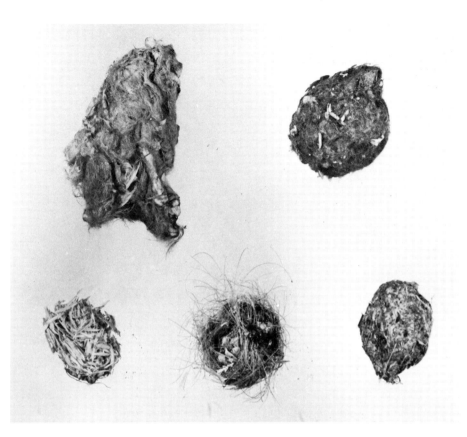

Both owl and kestrel (**bottom right**) pellets often reveal which small animals are active in an area.

them to tap their usual food supplies. These birds are able to feed on rubbish dumps and bird-tables, where efficient bills are less vital.

## Starling *Sternus vulgaris*

The starling was originally a woodland bird, breeding in tree holes. It soon became adapted to city life, nesting in the many crevices in buildings. Its natural talent for mimicking other species soon extended to the imitation of car hooters, human laughter and telephones. As with the house sparrow, the starling population is impossible to census accurately in urban districts since so many of

the buildings are inaccessible, and it takes some courage on the part of an ornithologist to focus a pair of binoculars on the upper storeys of houses in search of birds carrying food. It seems likely, however, that between five and seven million pairs of starlings breed in Britain – a figure which prevents their true beauty being appreciated, since familiarity breeds contempt. Outside the breeding season the British population is greatly enlarged by Continental migrants attracted by our warmer, if wetter, climate.

When cold weather hits hard, starlings come into towns and cities which are always two or three degrees Centigrade warmer than the surrounding countryside. During 1983 and early 1984 Blackburn in Lancashire had

Partial albino blackbird.

a problem when up to a million starlings whirled and twittered in a noisy flock before roosting around the cathedral. Their droppings rained down on pedestrians and it was a full-time job for council workers to keep the pavements clean. They also make an unsightly mess of window-ledges and the walls of buildings. Many cities, including Dublin and London, have faced the starling menace from time to time and it may well be something of a health hazard. A far greater threat, however, is posed by the feral pigeon.

## Feral pigeon *Columba livia*

Feral pigeons are descended from the wild rock dove. They found the transition from towering cliffs to castle and cathedral walls easy to make and from these first tentative in-trusions have gone on to dominate towns. The true feral pigeon has two prominent black wing-bars, a white rump and a glossy green neck, particularly striking in the breeding bird, but the gene pool of the wild rock dove has been diluted by mating with escaped domestic pigeons and with racing birds, so considerable variations in plumage are found. Technically there is no difference between a dove and a pigeon; the two names are synonymous.

What damage do pigeons do in towns? There can be no doubt that there are too many of them, since in towns their natural predators are almost entirely absent. This, combined with a protracted breeding season and a life-span of up to thirty years, means that large populations build up very quickly, despite the fact that only two eggs are laid in each clutch. Pigeon droppings pose a considerable health

Robin's nest on garage shelf.

problem. When dry, they often contain a fungus called *Cryptococcus neoformans* which can cause damage to human skin and to the nervous system and lungs. Occasionally, its effect is lethal. Pigeons also carry Newcastle disease (fowl pest) and psittacosis, to which we all may now have some immunity. Today tetracyclin drugs quickly bring the disease under control, but those employed in cleaning public buildings need to wear protective clothing and masks. Pigeon droppings also damage limestone buildings and statues. The mess made by the droppings is sufficiently unpleasant and the cost of cleaning sufficiently high to warrant determined efforts to control the populations. These range from feeding restrictions to the use of nets or spraying roosts with repellent. Trapping and killing is also a possible method but is frowned upon by the public, as are more bizarre methods such as dosing their food with contraceptive chemicals or bombarding their night roosts with high-frequency sounds. One thing is certain. The pigeon is too well established as an urban creature for it ever to be beaten. The same applies to household pests lower down the evolutionary ladder such as cockroaches and blowflies.

## Insects

### Cockroaches

These insects belong to the order Dictyoptera and the sub-order Blattodea. They are typified by the tarsus area of the leg being divided into five separate joints and by the fact that they cannot jump, which distinguishes cockroaches from the grasshoppers and crickets

**Above and below** Starlings are beautiful birds, but occasionally occur with deformed bills.

which make up the order Orthoptera. In Britain there are six introduced species of cockroach: the common (*Blatta orientalis*), American (*Periplaneta americana*), Australian (*Periplaneta australasiae*), Surinam (*Pycnoscelus surinamensis*), German (*Blattella germanica*) and brown-banded (*Supella supellectilium*). In addition there are three native species: the dusky (*Ectobius lapponicus*), tawny (*Ectobius pallidus*) and lesser cockroach (*Ectobius panzeri*). These are all found in woodlands or on heaths and are not associated with buildings, so do not concern us here. The introduced species all originated in warm climates and are unable to survive out of doors except perhaps in rubbish tips and sewers, where decaying organic matter can raise the temperature often by several degrees.

## Life history of the cockroach

Domestic cockroaches are little affected by climate thanks to man's artificial heating systems, the efficiency of which have been found to affect their rate of development profoundly. The eggs are enclosed inside a purse-like structure called an ootheca, which is either carried by the female or deposited in some convenient cranny. In ideal conditions the young hatch in approximately three weeks. The young feed voraciously, as do the adults. Cockroaches are omnivorous, feeding not only on human food stores but also on woollen garments and on paper and wood. The young grow rapidly and look like small versions of the adult. At least six moults are required to accommodate this growth. The details vary with the individual species, which are described below.

## Common cockroach
*Blatta orientalis*

This large cockroach, often called the black beetle, is about 22mm (⁹/₁₀ inch) long. The males are dark reddish brown and have two pairs of wings, which are not very efficient. The female is almost black in colour and her wings are completely vestigial, though traces of them are visible. It is thought that the species reached Britain on trade ships from North Africa during the sixteenth century and had spread rapidly by the eighteenth. A scourge of bakeries and restaurants, the common cockroach also occurs occasionally in houses and in garden rubbish dumps. The ootheca contains up to eighteen eggs arranged in two rows, sixteen being the most likely number, and the hatchlings may go through between six and twelve moults before maturity is reached in anything from seven months to three years, depending upon temperature and food supply. Adults do not live longer than nine months, but a female can produce a large number of oothecae in this period. The species is difficult to eradicate because the flat body can be squeezed into gaps between skirting boards or behind water pipes. Like most cockroaches, they are nocturnal and are capable of very rapid movement.

## American cockroach
*Periplaneta americana*

The American cockroach (also known as the ship cockroach) can measure up to 39mm (1½ inches), the males tending to be larger than the females. Both sexes have wings. Africa is thought to be the place of origin rather than the New World, despite its name. However, it may well have been taken to America on slave ships and it is still a common inhabitant of ships' holds, from which it doubtless spread to warehouses and then to restaurants, refineries and other industrial buildings, and from these into the sewers. It is seldom found in houses.

The oothecae contain from six to eighteen eggs cemented into holes which are plugged by an oval secretion produced by the female. Hatching occurs at any time from one to three months, depending on temperature. After about ten moults, over a developmental period of from five months to one year, the

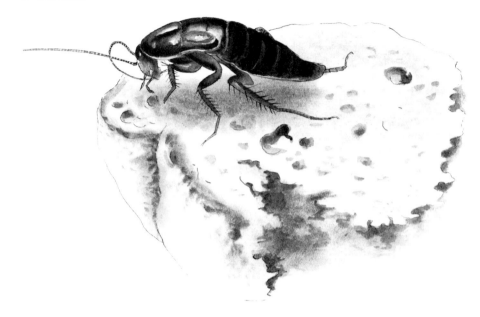

American cockroach on stale bread.

cockroach is sexually mature. Adults have been known to live as long as two years.

Again the diet is variable and when food is short some individuals turn cannibal, which may well explain why the females take so much trouble to conceal their oothecae.

## Australian cockroach
*Periplaneta australasiae*

The Australian cockroach also probably arrived in the Antipodes aboard ship from Africa or Asia and was then transported to Britain. It is somewhat smaller than its American cousin being about 30mm (1⅕ inch) in length. Both sexes are winged.

## Surinam cockroach
*Pycnoscelus surinamensis*

This is also true of the 18mm (⁷⁄₁₀ inch) Surinam cockroach, also of Asian origin and found in heated greenhouses. It is unique among our introduced species in being ovovi-

viparous, which means that the young hatch within the female, the oothecae being first extruded and then retracted into a brood patch.

## German cockroach
*Blattella germanica*

Other names for this cockroach include 'shiner', 'croton fly', 'big fly' and 'steam fly'. It originated in North Africa and is now found in dwelling houses as well as restaurants, industrial premises and, during the summer, in rubbish dumps. Both sexes are winged and seldom exceed 11mm (²⁄₅ inch), the female tending to be larger than her mate. They are usually coloured pale yellowy-brown with two longitudinal brown stripes on the pronotum – the area covering the dorsal surface of the first segment on the thorax.

## Brown-banded cockroach
*Supella supellectilium*

The brown-banded cockroach owes its name

to the band across the base of the forewings. These are developed more fully in the male than in the female. This species is a recent introduction to Britain from Africa and is found in houses and offices. It seldom exceeds 14mm (½ inch) in length. A distribution survey is needed both for this species and for cockroaches in general – yet another worthwhile project for co-ordinated groups of amateur naturalists armed with enthusiasm and an adequate reference library.

## Housefly *Musca domestica*

## Bluebottle *Calliphora vomitoria*

To fully comprehend how wildlife has adjusted to city life the urban naturalist should be prepared to study the life history of pests, including such creatures as flies. The housefly and the bluebottle are members of the Diptera order of insects, which are characterised by the presence of two pairs of wings, the second pair (called halteres) being modified as flight stabilisers and shaped like drumsticks. Both species feed through a long coiled tube called the proboscis. Digestive enzymes are pumped down this tube onto the food, then the soup-like product is sucked back into the mouth. Since the flies may feed on germ-ridden excrement then within minutes be feasting on human food, especially if it contains sugar, this method of feeding readily transmits germs. The hairy bodies of the flies carry large numbers of germs too, which is why houseflies are such a hazard to human health. Moreover, housefly eggs are laid on decaying matter, both animal and vegetable, whilst the female bluebottle, or blowfly, tends to seek out meat. In hot weather housefly eggs hatch out into legless larvae on the day following laying. Within a week the larva has eaten greedily and moulted twice to accommodate its rapid growth. After four days as a pupa a fertile adult emerges to continue the cycle. The cycle slows down in the winter when flies hibernate in buildings, but during the warmer months the housefly population rises rapidly as the flies breed in every house and open space in the city.

# 3 Walls and spaces

Open the pages of an A–Z of any large city and visualise the rows of buildings and the hustling traffic streaming between them. Then look more closely and note the areas of green, which are surprisingly numerous even in the centre of the city itself. Visit these areas and during your wanderings notice also how many temporary open spaces there are, as buildings are demolished and the sites await fresh development. Each of these areas has a surprising variety of plants and animals – for it makes little difference to a woodlouse if the wall in which it lives surrounds a forest or a clump of bird-sown elder, a country mansion or a London car-park, since the creature never travels further than a few yards from its place of birth.

This chapter describes the wildlife of these areas – first the plant and invertebrate life of the enclosing walls, then the species most likely to be found in the spaces themselves, including car-parks, railway sidings, roads and derelict sites, all of which are rich in fauna and flora.

## Walls

Like seaside cliffs and mountain rock faces, walls are not easy places for wildlife to colonise. They do, however, offer a unique opportunity for urban naturalists to observe the phenomenon of plant succession, as complex plants gradually strengthen their grip on a habitat first colonised by the simpler but less demanding plants. The usual sequence is:

Simple plants such
as algae and lichens
▽
liverworts
and mosses
▽

ferns
▽
herbs
▽
trees

## Simple plants

A close look at all but the most recently constructed walls will reveal a green and, when dry, dusty covering. If this is scraped off and examined under a magnifying glass, or preferably a microscope, one or more species of simple green plants of the genus *Pleurococcus* (also called *Protococcus*) will be found. The greatest concentrations of these algae seem to occur on north-facing surfaces. The plant is very resistant to pollution and its success may be independent of the surface on which it grows, though rough surfaces tend to be colonised before it spreads to smoother areas. The structure of the plant is very simple, as is its asexual method of reproduction which involves the rapid spread of cloned cells during dry, windy weather. Such conditions are not uncommon in towns, where the air is fanned into motion as air currents are created by busy traffic. *Pleurococcus* produces food from sunlight by photosynthesis and forms the base of a food pyramid. Vegetarian organisms, especially molluscs such as the garden snail (*Helix aspersa*), scrape the algae from the walls using a rasp-like organ called the radula. Many snails are in turn eaten by song thrushes. They reach the snail flesh by battering the shell against a stone and a thrush's anvil is found almost as often in towns as it is in the countryside. The resourceful birds have little trouble in finding acceptable nest sites often in the most unexpected places.

## Lichens

Lichens are also early colonists of walls and are ideally fitted to this purpose by their mode of life. They are really two organisms in one; an algal component provides food for the lichens, while a fungus produces an acid which eats into the stone and makes the anchorage more secure. This combination works well for both partners and is called symbiosis. Because of their intolerance to pollutants, lichens are useful indicators of the health of the atmosphere. Of the two partners, the fungal component appears to be the most vulnerable to pollution.

There are three basic types of lichen: crustose, foliose and fruticose. Crustose forms are more often found in cities than the less tolerant foliose types, which have a horizontal creeping body called a thallus, or the fruticose types in which the tassel-shaped thallus is attached only by its base.

Crustose lichens, as their name indicates, are flat and form a 'crust' on the rock, which makes them difficult to remove without damage. Like all lichens they grow slowly and the growth rate is affected by pollution. This makes it possible for the skilled worker to detect when pollution levels begin to rise in a town and at which point in time things begin to improve. The method is particularly accurate when the precise age of lichen-covered buildings is known or tombstones in churchyards carry dated inscriptions encrusted with lichen.

The fact that many lichens do not have common names sometimes deters the amateur naturalist from studying them, but with a little practice a few types which occur in towns can easily be recognised. *Squamaria* (*Leconora*) *muralis* is capable of covering a whole wall with a grey coat; even more tolerant of pollution is *Lepraria incana*, which looks at first like a fine grey-blue dust and often grows between tufts of maidenhair spleenwort, which owes its anchorage to the lichen.

## Liverworts and mosses

After the initial pioneering by algae and lichens, liverworts often find a niche – but only on wet walls. Some thirteen species of moss are also found regularly on the walls of towns and cities. The most common is the wall screw moss (*Tortula muralis*), while on the tops of walls are found the greater grey matted thread moss (*Bryum capillare*), the grey cushion moss (*Grimmin pulvinata*) and the silvery thread moss (*Bryum argentium*), which has proved hardy enough to survive in cracks between paving stones and is surprisingly tolerant of trampling. It is thought that silver thread moss spores are sometimes spread by human feet or by rain-water, and it has been established that detached pieces of moss can grow independently and become new plants.

The life-cycle of bryophytes (liverworts and mosses) consists of regular alternation of generations, the first called the sporophyte and the second the gametophyte. The latter tends to be flat and leaf-like and it carries both male and female reproductive organs, the 'sperms' reaching the 'eggs' by swimming through a film of water guided by a chemical attractant. This means that bryophytes are only able to grow in areas where there is a fairly regular supply of water at the time when the gametophyte plant is fertile. From the fertilised egg grows the sporophyte generation, which initially lives as a parasite on the gametophyte until strong enough to produce its own food by photosynthesis and obtain other essential elements from the substrate on which it grows. When mature this generation produces light spores which are spread by the wind. Those which fall on a suitable area germinate into a new gametophyte generation.

## Ferns

The pteridophytes, as ferns are called, have a similar life-cycle to that of mosses. The gametophyte generation, however, is much less important, though still dependent upon water for reproduction, and the sporophyte plant is almost totally dominant. Three species are likely to be found on town walls: maidenhair spleenwort, wall rue and the com-

**Above** *Pleurococcus* on tree bark.          **Below** Lichen (*Squamaria*) on stone.

**Above** Seedling moss.                    **Below** Maidenhair spleenwort.

mon polypody. A fourth species, the hart's tongue fern, turns up occasionally. Maidenhair spleenwort (*Asplenium trichomanes*), although more usually associated with upland regions where there is plenty of lime, also occurs in the crevices of walls pointed with mortar and may well have escaped from the physic gardens maintained by the old apothecaries, who frequently used the plant to treat diseases of the spleen – an example of the doctrine of signatures which was one of the principal tenets of medicinal botany for so long. The idea was that if part of a plant resembled a human organ, God had indicated by his signature that the plant could cure diseases of that organ. Many plants growing in towns have escaped from such collections.

Wall rue (*Asplenium ruta-muraria*) has adapted particularly well to life in towns. It appears to thrive in areas illuminated by street lighting, especially of the ultraviolet type.

The hart's tongue fern (*Phyllitis scolopendrium*) often thrives in the brickwork of roadside drains, in entrances to cellars and poking out through gratings. These habitats contain plenty of lime – ideal for this plant, which is a calcicolous (lime-loving) species growing naturally in the clints and grykes of upland limestone pavements. (Clints are the blocks of limestone and grykes are the cracks between them.)

# Higher plants

Once the pioneer plants have produced sufficient humus to clothe the naked cracks in the walls, the higher plants appear. Prominent amongst these are rosebay willowherb, herb Robert, ivy-leaved toadflax and wallflower.

## Rosebay willowherb
*Epilobium angustifolium*

This plant is believed to have been introduced from North America and to have spread throughout Britain along the developing railway system from the 1850s onwards. It was given an extra boost by bomb damage done in city centres during the Second World War. The species is often called fireweed, perhaps because of its ability to colonise devastated areas quickly. Doubtless this ability is due to the light, fluffy and mobile cottony seeds. Sir Edward Salisbury estimated that a single plant produces an average of 80,000 seeds. Research suggests that rosebay willowherb has been part of the British flora since the end of the Ice Age and that modern urban activities have favoured its spread. Its lovely pink blooms are a welcome attraction to all but gardeners who wish to grow something more exotic but often far less beautiful. The theory that the plant was introduced to Britain from North America may have some substance in that the species found in North America has twice as many chromosomes as the native British stock and both varieties occur in Britain. The plant's natural habitat seems to have been on rocky outcrops and since walls and crumbling rubble do not differ much from its native habitat they are readily colonised. It is also commonly found growing on banks beside railways, roads and motorways.

The leaves of rosebay willowherb are the favourite food of the larvae of the elephant hawk moth (*Deilephila elpenor*). Just after the Second World War, when London's bomb sites were ablaze with fireweed, the greenish adult moths with wings and body edged with red were perfectly camouflaged. The adult hawk moths, which have a wingspan of 10cm (4 inches), gather nectar from the flowers while their huge greenish-black caterpillars with their tapering bodies resembling elephants' trunks, gobble away at the leaves. When attacked or danger threatens, the larva stretches its body segments to expose large spots which flash like glaring eyes – a defence mechanism that deters many a potential predator and is especially effective at dawn and dusk, when the insect is active. It spends the day hiding among the roots of the willowherb, and is so well camouflaged that it is difficult to find.

Larvae of large elephant hawk moth.

# Herb Robert

*Geranium robertianum*

Like rosebay, herb Robert shows some degree of genetic variation. Three subspecies are now recognised, all preferring moderate shade and most often found growing on walls facing north and east. The origin of the name of this attractive though rather rancid-smelling little plant is not known with certainty but it may come from its association with the robin, which nests close to it in the crevices of walls. Other suggestions have linked it with St Robert of Salzburg, whose feast day is at the end of April when the flowers appear, or it may be a corruption of the Latin *ruber*, meaning red. The small pink blooms have five sepals, five petals and ten stamens, the flower-

ing period lasting until October, by which time the beaked fruits show clearly that herb Robert is a member of the cranesbill family. Herb Robert has one great advantage as far as the ecology of walls is concerned in that its leaves are slender and wide-spreading and so do not prevent light reaching the pioneer species beneath.

## Ivy-leaved toadflax

*Cymbalaria muralis*

This plant is thought to have spread from Italy and the Balkans across Europe and into Britain, almost certainly assisted by deliberate introductions into greenhouses and into gardens, where it flourishes on south-west facing walls. There is no doubt that it is now thoroughly at home, having a self-fertilising mechanism as well as being cross-pollinated by bees. Some of the sweet, sticky seeds are carried by ants, but the plant is able to sow its own seeds deep in the dark crevices of walls. Once the seed is set, the flower stalks grow away from the light – technically called negative phototropism – and into the wall.

## Wallflower *Cheiranthus cheiri*

The wallflower is an alien perennial with a strong, pleasant smell which made it popular with the gardeners who introduced it from the eastern Mediterranean at a time when city streets stank abominably. It does not colonise new walls to any great extent, but in ancient heaps of rubble it often makes a most attractive show. Its seeds are also spread by ants, which with woodlice and spiders are the typical invertebrates of walls.

## Invertebrates

Even a casual poke about in the crevices of a wall reveals a surprisingly large population of invertebrates and an interesting variety of species. It is impossible to collect them by hand, but an efficient instrument for this purpose, which can be made for just a few pence, is a pooter. A pooter is made from a glass

**Above** Large elephant hawk moth.

**Above left** Rosebay willowherb.

**Left** Herb Robert.

**Opposite** Ivy-leaved toadflax.

vessel fitted with a cork bung, into which lead two glass or plastic tubes. One tube has a mouthpiece which can be sucked to produce a vacuum in order to draw small animals into the pooter. These then fall to the bottom of the vessel and can be examined at leisure. Many of the old ecology books aimed at schools and universities recommend killing the specimens in 60 per cent alcohol, but that is not usually necessary and after identification the animals can be returned preferably, but not necessarily, to the same wall.

## Ants

Of all the social insects, ants show the greatest degree of organisation, their colonies being more permanent and more flexible than those of wasps and bees. The preferred habitat of ants is grassland and man's early activities in clearing woodland must have been beneficial to the growth of ant populations, whilst the trampling effect of urban man is detrimental. Buildings well endowed with walled gardens encourage substantial local increases, especially of the black ant (*Lasius niger*), which finds south-facing walls populated by wallflower and ivy-leaved toadflax an ideal habitat. Occasionally tropical species, especially Pharoah's ant (*Monomorium pharaonis*), occupy centrally heated buildings. They find exotic plants and sugar bowls attractive, and thrive if such amenities are present.

The pooter of the urban naturalists is most likely to pick up specimens of the black ant. This species illustrates the basic structure of an ant's body particularly clearly. As with other insects, the body is divided into head, thorax and abdomen, but, as with the rest of the Hymenoptera, which include wasps and bees, there is an additional feature. One or two of the abdominal segments have evolved into a narrow tube – a structure known as the petiole, which gives the body remarkable flexibility. A hymenopteran is therefore said to consist of a mesoma, made up of the thorax plus one abdominal segment, and the hind

body, known as the gaster, which is made up of the final seven body segments, although usually not all of these are visible. The tip of the ant's mesoma can thus be brought up to its jaws, enabling it to cut up its prey or enemy with its mouthparts and squirt venom, a derivative of formic acid, into the wound. The head is also very flexible, as are the most important sense organs, the hinged antennae, which are made up of a base (the scape) and a many-jointed club-shaped structure called the funiculus. These organs are able to respond to sound, vibrations, touch and chemical stimuli. Many insects have compound eyes, often made up of thousands of separate cells called ocelli, but the eyes of ants are never highly developed, since they spend most of their time deep in the confines of their nest.

Above Ant in garden.

Both the queen ant and the short-lived but much more numerous males are winged and at a pre-ordained chemical signal triggered by a calm, warm day towards the end of summer, the soaring nuptial flight takes place. This event is eagerly welcomed by hordes of hungry birds, including starlings, martins, black-headed gulls and house sparrows. Since the winged males greatly outnumber the females the chances of a queen being among the victims is slight, and after she has been fertilised she carries sufficient sperm to establish and maintain a colony. After removing her wings by rubbing them on a convenient stone, she seeks out a suitable nest site and begins to lay eggs, her initial food requirements being met by the reabsorption of her now unwanted but once substantial flight muscles. The first eggs laid develop into larvae, which she feeds with her own saliva. They develop into workers (which are infertile males, without wings) and wingless females, whose sole function is to feed the now hungry queen, though it is the workers that bring back food, both animal and vegetable, to the nest for the queen and the developing larvae to eat. Ants are particularly attracted to sweet substances and this is often

Above During the breeding season queen and male ants develop wings.

Below Woodlouse (Oniscus asellus).

Worker ant.

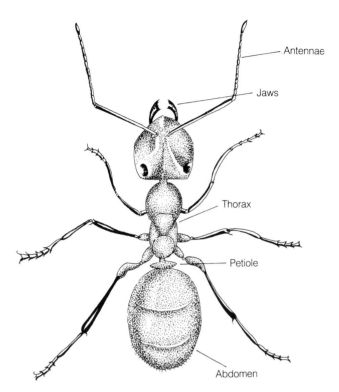

Antennae

Jaws

Thorax

Petiole

Abdomen

the cause of their downfall when they live close to human habitation, since, sometimes, poisoned bait is eagerly carried back to the nest. Any pathway to rich food supplies is marked by the workers with a chemical known as a pheromone. It is also their job to construct new galleries as the colony expands.

A fascinating piece of ant behaviour is seen when they climb trees and bushes to feed upon the sticky substance called honeydew which oozes from the abdomen of greenfly. This 'milking' is clearly part of the ants' genetic memory, since they even go to the trouble of carrying greenfly larvae back to the nest, care for them during the winter, then 'put them out to grass' when warmer weather returns. Nevertheless, ants, like wasps, consume large numbers of other insect larvae, many of which, such as wireworms, harm plants or crops, thus doing mankind a good turn.

Eventually the queen lays a batch of fertilised eggs that develop into young queens and a batch of unfertilised eggs that develop into winged males which have only one job – to fertilise a virgin queen. Thus the world of the ant is almost totally matriarchal, with the role of the male being reduced to one of pure reproduction.

## Woodlice

Found in every urban situation, including most old houses and walls, woodlice can be captured using an easily constructed variation of the pitfall trap. A wide-mouthed bottle is lined with moss and fitted with a bung through which a funnel is pushed. A triangular structure is formed from bent wire, baited with strong-smelling bait and placed inside the funnel. The apparatus is then hidden in vegetation and pushed against a wall, so that invertebrates climbing in to reach the bait fall through the wire triangle and into the moss below. The trap will also capture millipedes and a host of beetles. Estimates of the woodlouse population can be made by the trap-and-retrap methods using a pitfall trap of this kind – or, since they are nocturnal, they can be captured at night with a torch. They are easily marked, using nail varnish. Woodlice often frequent damp areas in walls, cellars and under stones, but prefer warm, dark places. This can be demonstrated by means of a choice chamber, which can be made by dividing a circular tray into four interconnecting sections, two of these being covered to create darkness and two left uncovered so they are open to the light. One of the dark sections and one of the light ones are kept moist; and the others are kept dry by means of calcium chloride, which absorbs water from the atmosphere. Thus the animals have a choice between dry-dark, moist-dark, dry-light and moist-light. When woodlice are placed randomly in the chamber they soon move into the section which is dark and damp. A choice chamber can be purchased from a biological supplier, but I have found a circular cheese box covered with aluminium foil makes quite an acceptable substitute.

It is often thought that woodlice emerge from their damp hideaways at night solely to hunt for their food, which consists mainly of rotting vegetation. Recent research suggests that their imperfect control over the water content of their bodies may not only cause them to dry up quickly but also to soak up water when a surfeit is available and thus become bloated. Therefore they may require periods out in the open in order to 'dry out'. However, not all authorities accept this theory and more research is needed.

In Britain some forty-two species occur, of which twenty-eight or twenty-nine are native, the others having been accidentally introduced among shipments of plants. Two common species in urban situations are

Seven-spot ladybirds mating.

*Oniscus asellus* and *Porcellio scaber*. Both these species are attracted to walls containing mortar since they require the calcium salts in the lime in order to manufacture their external skeletons.

There are three basic regions making up the body of a typical woodlouse. The small head has powerful jaws and bears one large and one tiny pair of antennae. The thorax, or pereion, is protected by seven overlapping plates, which look like roof tiles, and seven pairs of limbs are carried below this armament. The abdomen, called the pleon, is divided into six segments and has four protective plates. The last of these is triangular and covers the telson, the last segment of the abdomen. The first five segments of the pleon have limb-like structures which function as gills and betray the aquatic ancestry of the woodlouse, although their rudimentary adaptation to terrestrial life is seen in the development of tiny breathing tubes called pseudo-tracheae. A careful look at the pleonic limbs reveals tiny white dots, which are the openings to these tubes. The final pair of appendages are called uropods, but these are sensory rather than respiratory in function. They also produce, as do some of the other body segments, unpleasant secretions that help protect the woodlouse from its many enemies, which include birds, toads, shrews, some ground beetles and numerous species of spiders.

## Myriapoda

The myriapoda is an ideal name for a class of arthropods (invertebrate animals with jointed legs) which includes the centipedes and millipedes. Millipedes can be recognised by the presence of two pairs of appendages on each body segment while centipedes have only one pair of appendages per segment.

## Beetles

Of all the groups of animals found in the world today none is more widespread or numerous than the beetles, which include the ubiquitous seven-spot ladybird (*Coccinella septempunctata*). Many are associated with fresh water, but they have also evolved efficient structures to enable them to fly, protect themselves from predators and conserve essential water. They are members of the insect family Coleoptera typified by having their forewings modified into hard wing cases called elytra. These meet to form a straight line down the back, a feature sufficient to establish that the animal is a beetle. The hind wings can be modified for flight, as they are in the ladybird, but they are often reduced or absent altogether. The mouthparts are often adapted for chewing other animals and the ladybird is very helpful in the destruction of greenfly and other aphids. Beetles show what is known as a complete metamorphosis and four stages can be recognised in the life-cycle – egg, larva, pupa and adult. Over 4,000 species are found in Britain alone and so the beginner should not become discouraged if a specimen cannot be identified with certainty and be happy if the insect can be placed into its correct family.

Garden spider.

Web of garden spider (*Araneus diadematus*).

## Spiders

Ever since Miss Patience Muffet was frightened by a spider, this useful and intriguing group of animals has been sadly maligned. When it is realised that Dr Thomas Muffet (1553–1604) was a physician and an expert on spiders who believed that eating them cured digestive disorders and coughs, and that he invented the rhyme to make his daughter take her medicine, we may understand why there has been a reluctance to get to grips with their biology.

Spiders, like insects, are jointed-legged animals belonging to the Arthropoda phylum. They are distinguished from insects by having eight legs (not six) and a body divided into two parts (not three). The cephalothorax is separated from the larger, often bulbous, abdomen by a narrow waist.

Spiders belong to the class Arachnida, which also includes mites and harvestmen. There are almost 600 species on the British list, many of them occurring in the urban situation. Keys are available which enable many of these species to be identified. Spiders are carnivorous and as they feed voraciously on many invertebrate pests their presence must be considered beneficial to human enterprises. Spiders do not have the powerful mouthparts typical of many insects. Instead they have a small mouth to suck the juices from their prey, which is subdued by venom injected into a puncture wound inflicted by fangs. Some tropical species – but not, contrary to popular belief, the tarantulas and none of the British species – are able to penetrate human skin. All spiders produce silk, but they do not all spin webs. Their eggs are, however, wrapped in silk cocoons, the delicate threads being produced by glands in the abdomen, each opening to the exterior via a spinneret. Different types of silk do different jobs – covering egg cocoons, web production, entombing prey and making the silken ropes on which spiders swing. The silk is pulled out of the spinneret by the vigorous action of the back pair of legs, not forced out under pressure from within the abdomen. Silk threads no longer required are usually eaten by the spider – an example of nature's built-in attitude to conservation.

Spiders possess a pair of palps at the front end. In the males these are club-shaped and used to carry the sperm and fertilise the female. In many species the male first spins a tiny sperm web and then squirts a packet of semen onto it before picking it up in his palps. The courtship display is complex and involves the male twanging on the female's larger web like a skilled harpist. He needs to be skilful so that she can distinguish between mate and food, but she may still decide to eat him once he has deposited his sperm. Eggs are laid in silken cocoons, which usually survive the winter before the spiderlings emerge the following spring. After several moults they are themselves able to breed.

In towns the species most likely to be encountered are the garden spider (*Araneus diadematus*) and the crow spider (*Zygrella* × *notata*), which is the one likely to be found on walls, in the corners of rooms or in the bath or kitchen sink. The wolf spider (*Pisaura mirabilis*), an active hunter, is often found scavenging on roadsides and around rubbish dumps. To identify the less common spiders a good key is required, but many species can be identified by the webs they produce. Most species, if captured and held prisoner for a while in a secure box, will soon spin a web. This can be preserved by spraying it with hair lacquer or white aerosol paint and a reference collection can be made by mounting webs on black card and covering them with transparent paper such as cling-film. Habitat preferences can be investigated by use of a choice chamber, though the experiment will take longer than with woodlice. Spiders are solitary and aggressive predators, and in pursuit of prey many wolf spiders venture out into open spaces where they may themselves fall victim to small mammals and birds.

## Open spaces

The open spaces of a city tend to attract rubbish, including discarded bottles – and empty milk bottles are probably responsible for killing more small mammals than any other cause, since the empty bottles attract invertebrates which are unable to escape from the smooth glass walls and their decaying bodies in turn attract small mammals which are then trapped and die. Although rather unpleasant, an excellent method of surveying which mammals are present in the open spaces of a town is to collect the animal remains from these bottles. Sweet-smelling disinfectant plus a little bleach removes the worst of the problem and it is a simple matter, requiring just a little practice, to identify small mammals from the pattern of their teeth. Rats and mice, for example, are typified by having cheek-teeth marked with irregular grinding surfaces. This contrasts with those of the voles, which have a clear zigzag pattern on their surface. Town dwellers will be surprised how often skulls of short-tailed field voles turn up. These little hamster-like creatures are well able to survive in cities by gnawing away at the roots of grass tufts. Also present on many occasions will be the remains of the common shrew (*Sorex araneus*), which has long incisors with each tooth etched around in red – a distinctive feature of the family.

## Birds

Two species of bird in particular have taken advantage of wasteland in and near city centres. These are the black redstart, which invaded London after the Second World War, and the little ringed plover, which now nests regularly in abandoned dockland and disused

Black redstart (cock).

steelworks in many cities, including London, Manchester and Liverpool.

## Black redstart
*Phoenicurus ochruros*

The black redstart is afforded special protection in Great Britain under Schedule I of the Protection of Birds Act 1954–67, but the law is even more difficult to enforce than usual since this is the only rare bird totally associated with truly urban and highly industrialised areas. Its loud ringing song can be clearly heard early on a summer's morning but is soon drowned by the noise of the city or factories, so that even the most strident efforts of the cock are quickly muffled. The mature male is dark grey above and has a distinctive black throat and breast, against which the white wing patch shows up clearly. There is also a faint eye ring, more obvious in some individuals than in others. The undertail coverts are white in the male, while the rust-red tail of the dull sooty-brown female is indicative of the bird's name.

The nest is constructed on ledges, on stones or under eaves. Between four and six eggs are laid towards the end of April and are incubated by the hen alone. Since the male does not help in nest building either, he plays no part until the incubation period of twelve to thirteen days is complete. The cock then takes an active part in feeding the chicks with invertebrates and they are able to fly in under eighteen days, leaving time for two or sometimes three broods.

There are records of black redstarts breeding in Britain in 1845 and in 1909. The next record is of two pairs breeding on the coastal

Little ringed plover about to incubate her eggs.

cliffs of Sussex in 1923 and three years later a pair nested in the derelict site of the 1925 Wembley Exhibition. Then in 1941, after the colonisation of bomb sites in London and other cities, the spread accelerated and has continued ever since, with the birds making use of abandoned railway stations, gasworks, ironworks and power stations. The population still does not exceed 100 pairs, but there are increased numbers of winter visitors and the future for this most urban of birds looks secure.

## Little ringed plover
*Charadrius dubius*

This bird was unknown as a breeding species in Britain before 1938 when a pair bred at Tring reservoir in Hertfordshire. Like the black redstart, it still has Schedule I protection in Britain. The population now exceeds 500 pairs, many on disused industrial sites such as railway sidings, derelict or filled-in docks, rubbish dumps and demolished factories. The little ringed plover is distinguished from the more common and predominantly coastal ringed plover (*Charadrius hiaticula*) by its size of 15cm (6 inches), compared with the 18cm (7½ inches) of *C. hiaticula*, and by the complete absence of a wing bar in flight. The little ringed plover also has a prominent yellow ring round its eye and the flesh-coloured legs never flash bright orange, as the ringed plover's do.

The little ringed plover is a summer visitor and in the urban situation it comes to no harm feeding on spiders, snails and sometimes, especially after rain, on worms washed out

**Above** Lapwing incubating.                    **Below** Ragwort.

from their burrows. Its four eggs are laid in May among grassy tufts or even among the debris of buildings. Both sexes incubate the eggs and the incubation period lasts almost a month. The young leave the nest when they are dry and follow their parents for some time after their first flight, which is normally attempted by the twenty-fifth day after hatching. There is usually time for only one brood to be raised, but if the first clutch of eggs is lost a repeat clutch is often attempted.

Most urban naturalists are excited when they discover black redstarts or little ringed plovers breeding in their neighbourhood, but should resist the temptation to disclose their whereabouts. In urban areas, where the wildlife is already under greater pressure, conservation is even more important than in most other habitats – with the possible exception of those which are heavily farmed. Some idea of the resilience of nature can be gained from a brief consideration of railway embankments and motorway verges – open spaces which often penetrate into the very heart of a city. Airports too have their share of interesting breeding birds, including the lapwing (*Vanellus vanellus*) and the oystercatcher (*Haematopus ostralegus*).

## Roads and railways

Prominent among plants spread by the railway system are common ragwort (*Senecio jacobaea*), which is a native of Britain, and Oxford ragwort (*Senecio squalidus*), which is a native of Sicily where it grows on the volcanic ash of Mount Etna. Oxford ragwort was introduced into the botanic gardens in Oxford about 1750. It escaped first onto the walls and then along the expanding railway system, finding the clinker produced by the steam engines very like its native habitat on Etna. Present in the same habitat may be common groundsel (*Senecio vulgaris*), which is often confused with Oxford ragwort. However, the leaves of common groundsel are less finely toothed and grow at regular intervals up the stem, which is naked at the base, whereas Oxford ragwort has a sprawl of leaves at the base and the upper leaves clasp closely round the stem. Also, the flowers of Oxford ragwort are larger and, when open, look rather like yellow daisies, with a ray of slightly ragged petals.

Many railways have now closed, but what was a human social tragedy in some areas has been a boon for wildlife and linear nature reserves have developed in an amazingly short space of time. If local authorities can be prevented from landscaping railway embankments (which usually entails ripping out all pioneer flowers and shrubs and planting clinically manicured grass) they can provide the most important wildlife refuge in the whole of the city. No account of urban ecology would be complete without some reference to the work of the Department of Plant Biology at the University of Newcastle-upon-Tyne. In the autumn 1982 issue of *Country-Side*, the journal of the British Naturalists' Association, one of the team, Nick Scott, wrote:

It was in the mid-1960s that the application of salt to roadsides in winter reached the heavy rates known today. Soon after that there were several reports of high levels of salt in vergeside soils and in areas where ice and snow were common and salinity levels high, roadside vegetation began to be damaged. This was particularly so in North-Eastern England where, as well as severe winters, precipitation is comparatively low and so salt is not so quickly washed out during the summer. In the North-East some roadside grass swards were completely killed off for up to three metres from the road.

In 1975, whilst undertaking a vegetation survey of A1 verges, Paul Matthews came upon some unusual grasses. Newcastle's Plant Biology Department, in which Paul

was working, does not like to admit that it took a while for anyone to name these first grasses. It was not that they were unfamiliar, it was the unusual context they were in. For they were reflexed saltmarsh grass (*Puccinellia distans*) and common saltmarsh grass (*Puccinellia maritima*), two grasses that botanists associate with the coast. *Puccinellia maritima* is the dominant grass on most saltmarshes, giving a low, thick, mat-like sward. *Puccinellia distans* is found in saltmarshes where they are disturbed by cattle grazing or trampling. Since that first find we have discovered some thirteen maritime species on North-East England's roadsides, including sea

**Left** Oystercatchers nesting on an aerodrome.

**Below** Sea aster.

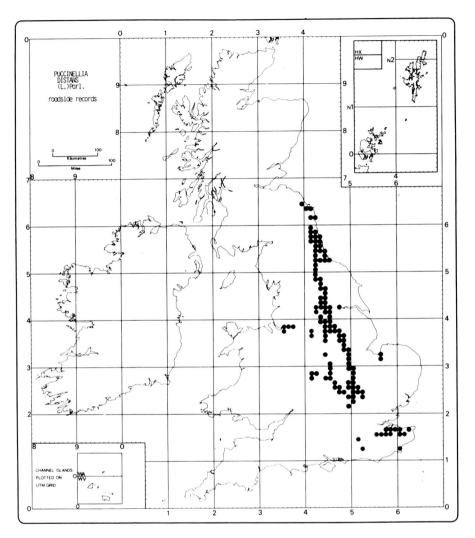

The distribution of *Puccinellia distans* on British roadsides.

aster (*Aster tripolium*), sea plantain (*Plantago maritima*), scurvy grass (*Cochlearia officinalis*), the two sea spurreys (*Spergularia media, S. marina*) and annual seablite (*Suaeda maritima*).

Maritime plants have also now been found elsewhere on roadsides in Britain.

These reports, together with records sent in by local botanists, have enabled us to map the roadside distribution of these species throughout Britain. While the grass *Puccinellia distans* is now widespread, all the other species are confined to the North-East of England and Kent, where sea aster, sea spurrey and sea barley (*Hordeum murinum*) occur.

One of the most interesting questions

Pineapple weed.

Thus it would seem most likely that these plants have reached the roadside habitat from the coast by carriage on vehicle tyres or undercarriages. Once established on roadsides, they are able to spread quickly by the seed being swept along in the slipstream of passing vehicles. Such a means of distribution would explain why some species have been much more successful in rapidly colonising this new habitat than others. *Puccinellia distans* in particular, but also the lesser sea spurrey (*Spergularia marina*), have spread very quickly. Both are adapted to disturbed saline sites and occur in such habitats on the coast. Both are short-lived and produce large quantities of light seed.

arising from these finds is, 'Where do the plants come from?' The obvious and most likely possibility is the local coast. After all, the two areas with a large roadside, maritime flora are coastal, and both have sites where vehicles can drive over saltmarshes. In Kent there is a continuous distribution of *Puccinellia distans* from the Isle of Sheppey, where cars cross saltmarshes, along the A249 till that road joins the roads on which the rest of the maritime species occur. In North-East England the causeway to Holy Island crosses a saltmarsh and is only five miles from the A1. Also the Tees-side petroleum industry is built amidst the remnants of a large saltmarsh. The widespread *Puccinellia distans* is now a long way from the coast, but still most populations can be traced back along roads to coastal *Puccinellia distans* sites where there is vehicular access.

The work of the Newcastle team underlines how readily plants can spread into urban situations. Next time you are in town, look out for pineapple weed (*Matricaria matricarioides*), which can be identified by its greenish-yellow flower head and feathery leaves. It looks like an unripe member of the daisy family, but crush a leaf and the characteristic smell of pineapples is immediately apparent. It is probably a native of north-eastern Asia but has now spread throughout Europe, North America and New Zealand thanks to the tough seeds, which travel in the treads of car tyres and are washed off by rain. I once knew a naturalist who washed his car tyres, then went out for a long drive. On his return he rinsed the tyres and collected 819 seeds, from which he successfully germinated 13 herbs, including pineapple weed, herb Robert, daisy, dandelion and shepherd's purse.

# 4 Parks

All Britain's cities are well provided for in terms of municipal parks, most of which were established during the heyday of Victorian affluence and civic pride. Before the war municipal parks were tended by armies of gardeners; but in the 1960s and 1970s, with rising labour costs, the neat flower-beds and concrete or asphalt paths became expensive to maintain, and park-keepers increasingly had recourse to the liberal use of insecticides and weedkillers that destroy or deter wildlife which would otherwise find areas of grass and trees attractive. In recent years, however, there has been a swing towards the idea of more 'natural' parks, with imaginatively laid out nature trails run by a warden from an information centre and used to good effect by parties of school children.

Naturalists, I suspect, rarely take full advantage of their local parks, preferring to journey out into the countryside in search of rarities, while missing the abundance of interesting wildlife to be found nearer home. This chapter describes first the parkland shrubs and trees, then the undergrowth and finally the wildlife associated with park lakes.

## Trees and shrubs

### Rhododendrons  *Rhododendron* spp
Those who design and maintain parks tend to prefer exotic trees, and rhododendrons are the dominant species in the majority of parks. Their colourful blooms are a delight to all, but there is a price to pay for their beauty since their leaves decay slowly and are highly acidic. As a result, the run-off into watercourses has a detrimental effect upon crustaceans and

molluscs, which are unable to build their shells in acid conditions. Rhododendron is not a single species but a huge genus of plants, including trees and shrubs, both evergreen and deciduous, as well as numerous hybrids, which makes identification difficult. The genus also includes azaleas, most of which are deciduous and have funnel-shaped flowers. Rhododendrons now cover large areas of the temperate zones of the Northern hemisphere and are also abundant in the Himalayas up to 5,800m (16,000 feet) and throughout South-East Asia, Australia and New Zealand. Most of the azaleas are native either to North America or to the area around Japan. Like most of the genus, they favour acid soils and their only advantage to wildlife lies in the tangled cover they provide for nesting birds, especially mistle and song thrushes and blackbirds.

### Plane  *Platanus* spp
The plane tree is typical of parks and city streets since it is highly resistant to atmospheric pollution, having bark which peels off and keeps the breathing holes (called lenticels) open. Most plane trees are hybrids of the Oriental plane (*Platanus orientalis*), a native of Asia Minor, and the North American plane (*Platanus occidentalis*). It is thought that the cross arose accidentally in Oxford about 1670. Although the hybrid plane occasionally sets seed, town planners usually prefer to propagate by cuttings.

The cone-shaped buds, arranged alternately along the stem, are protected not only by single green scales but also by the scars remaining from the previous year's fallen

London plane (*Platanus* × *hybrida*).

leaves. Each palm-shaped leaf is divided into five broad lobes and has a long stalk, which is hollow at the base. The bud for the next year lies snugly within this space. The catkin flowers and fruits are produced in strange round structures, which accounts for the American name for the species, 'bobbles'.

Plane trees are planted in towns because of their resistance to soot-laden atmospheres – which was a serious problem in the days when most industries and all domestic buildings burned coal. Close examination of plane tree trunks often reveals specimens of moths, including the peppered moth, which illus-

trates a phenomenon known as industrial melanism.

## Peppered moth *Biston betularia*

This moth was first investigated by Kettlewell, who noticed that in country districts the species was light in colour and possessed a considerable degree of camouflage against the bark of trees. In the grime of central Manchester, however, a black form, *Biston betularia carbonaria*, was found, which enjoyed the same protection against soot-stained trunks. It is this evolution of a darker colour in urban surroundings that is known as industrial melanism. Birds such as the dunnock (*Prunella modularis*) that occur in both town

Industrial melanism shown by the peppered moth.

and country eat the peppered moth. In towns the pale form of the moth would be easily seen, while in the country the reverse is true, hence the higher proportion of the dark form in urban populations. Manchester's first black form was recorded in 1850 and by 1950 more than 95 per cent were found to be of the *carbonaria* form. Since the Clean Air Acts came into operation this figure has fallen steadily. In Burnley, for example, the proportion dropped from 82 per cent in 1961 to 57 per cent in 1984. In what is regarded as a classic experiment, Kettlewell released large numbers of both pale and melanic peppered moths into the countryside of Dorset and the smog of Birmingham. His results show quite clearly that evolution by natural selection works much more quickly than was previously supposed.

The typical peppered moth has white wings covered with varying amounts of black. The female, which is on the wing from May to July, lays her eggs on a variety of trees and shrubs, including oak, rose, bramble, birch, elm, plum and many other fruit trees. The caterpillars, which are greenish with a few purplish spots, are busy eating until September or occasionally October, when they pupate until the following spring. Industrial melanism is not restricted to the peppered moth and has been found in ladybirds and in several other moth species, including the mottled beauty (*Cleora repandata*), the scalloped hazel (*Gonodontis bidendata*), the waved umber (*Hemerophila abruptoria*) and the nut tree tussock (*Colocasia coryli*).

Most moths are nocturnal, but it can be difficult to go 'mothing' in the local parks at night. Even if they are open, nocturnal prowlers tend to attract the attention of the park wardens or police. By far the best way is to obtain permission from the local warden or parks department or find out what to do from a local naturalists' group. You will find that most naturalists concern themselves with birds and flowers, whilst the Lepidoptera come way down their list of priorities. Even lepidopterists give more time to the diurnal butterflies than they do to night-flying moths. For this reason moth enthusiasts often find themselves breaking new ground. Larvae can easily be collected by beating vegetation and holding an inverted umbrella (almost as good as a specially purchased beating tray) under the branches. Moth caterpillars are notoriously difficult to identify and, although with practice you can learn to recognise the various species, the beginner is better employed capturing adults. This can be done by means of a battery-operated moth trap or by covering a large piece of card with a harmless glue into which the moths fly. The cheapest method is to paint a mixture of sugar, beer and treacle onto the trees, though not all moth species are attracted to this bait. The trees are visited at night when torchlight will reveal drunken moths enjoying the feast, so that they are easily captured. Again the conservation aspect of a naturalist's work must be stressed and care should be taken not to injure them and wherever possible the moths should be returned into the wild. They are an important link in the food chain and provide food for bats, a most underrated group of mammals.

## Pipistrelle bat

*Pipistrellus pipistrellus*

Like all other British species, the pipistrelle is insectivorous and finds moths a particularly nutritious mouthful. An investigation of hollow trees or the debris removed from the eaves of buildings often reveals the tiny skeletons of bats. The dental pattern of the pipistrelle is:

$$2 \times \left[ 1\frac{2}{3} \, C \, \frac{1}{1} \, PM \, \frac{2}{2} \, M \, \frac{3}{3} \right] = 34$$

This formula shows that on each side of its jaw the bat has two incisors on the top and three on the bottom, one canine tooth, two premolars and three molar teeth on both the bottom and upper jaws. With this fine set of teeth the pipistrelle is well-equipped as a predator. It locates its food by producing a series of high-pitched squeaks that function like a highly sophisticated radar system. Moths react to the squeaks by producing their own sounds, which effectively jam the bat's signal. The next time you stroll through your park at dusk and watch bats hawking through the trees you will be witnessing a fight to death, with all nature's weaponry being tuned to a high degree of efficiency.

Flight is the most energetic form of locomotion and since their wings are made of skin, not feathers, and their bones are solid, not hollow, bats are heavier than birds and so need more energy. Bats mate late in the year, but the female retains the sperm within her uterus throughout hibernation and the egg which she produces is fertilised when she

Pipistrelle bats roosting together to conserve heat.

awakes from her sleep. The young are usually born in June and remain with their mothers in separate nursing colonies for two months before becoming independent.

Bats require three things from the environment – food, shelter and water. All these are present in parks where there are hollow trees in which they can roost and hibernate. Hollow trees also provide nesting sites for birds, and both fungi and insects thrive on the rotting wood. What is, in fact, needed in every park is a wild corner containing birch trees and a tangle of nettles and other undergrowth.

## Birch *Betula* spp

There are two species of birch native to Britain, the hairy birch (*Betula pubescens*), which has downy twigs, and the silver birch, which is now called *Betula pendula* since the branches hang in delightfully shady arches. Weeping birches are a distinctive feature of many urban parks. Both species require full light to grow but stand up to wind and frost, which makes them ideal pioneer trees, and in areas where new parks are being created on former industrial spoil heaps the planting of birches, which grow surprisingly quickly, enables dramatic improvements to be made. However, foresters regard birches as nursery trees, since they seldom reach a hundred years of age before decay sets in.

Naturalists often find themselves at odds with park authorities who view dead trees as an eyesore and fear that rotten branches will drop on visitors. Obviously dangerous trees should be felled, but many can safely be left to provide nesting holes for starlings and great spotted woodpeckers, loose bark behind which treecreepers can nest and hollow crowns ideal for tawny owls.

## Great spotted woodpecker
*Dendrocopos major*

The great spotted woodpecker is at home both in woodland and parkland and its drum-

ming is a feature of many urban areas. The bird is about 23cm (9 inches) long and its plumage is basically black and white, the forehead being white and the crown black. The cock is distinguished from the hen by the bright red band across his nape. The undertail coverts are red and there is a white shoulder patch. The looping flight across a clearing between trees also makes for easy recognition. The chisel-like bill makes short work of the toughest trunks, but a nice soft birch full of insect larvae is especially welcome. To soften the effect of this battering, woodpeckers have extra air passages in the skull and very powerful neck muscles. Slow-motion photography has revealed that during the drumming, which is a part of the bird's breeding behaviour, as many as twenty blows may be

Bracket fungus on birch eventually produces a good habitat for insects and birds.

Great spotted woodpeckers often visit town bird-tables and breed in parks.

Tawny owl – a common parkland bird.

struck in one second. Serious research is being done into the design of the skull in the hope that it may help to improve the efficiency of motorcycle crash helmets.

Whilst drumming or feeding the great spotted woodpecker is able to maintain its position by means of its long toes, two pointing forwards and two to the rear. It also leans backwards on its tail, of which the two central tail feathers are specially strengthened. The tongue is extremely long and mobile and pushes its way into every nook and crevice in search of the larvae of wood-boring insects, which form the bulk of its diet. If the going gets tough, the bird will also eat fruits, seeds and nuts, and will even open the cones of exotic evergreens. It also visits bird-tables in winter.

After the nest hole has been excavated the female lays between four and seven glossy white eggs and incubates them, with only a little help from her mate, for about sixteen days. The young are fed by both sexes and can fly when they are about three weeks old. If a

## Treecreeper  *Certhia familiaris*

The treecreeper is so secretive in its habits that, unless a properly organised census is carried out, its presence is often overlooked in urban parkland. (The British Trust for Ornithology has developed a routine for carrying out a 'common bird census' and this scheme should be encouraged in every urban park.) Treecreepers are sometimes double-brooded and need to produce many young because they have numerous enemies, including the tawny owl.

## Owls

The tawny owl (*Strix aluco*) is present and usually breeding in most town parks and can be an important factor in controlling rodents, which are attracted to the scraps of food brought for birds by visitors. There is no doubt, however, that many small birds fall victim to the efficiency of the owl's hunting technique, keen eyes and powerful talons. I have often sat in my local park during the evening and listened to a group of small birds mobbing a tawny owl. All species combine to dive-bomb a roosting owl and I am sure this is intelligent behaviour designed to move the predator out of the area before it gets dark and the bird becomes a threat. Although absent from the Isle of Man and Ireland, the tawny owl is very common in the rest of the British Isles and there may be as many as 100,000 breeding pairs. The bird measures some 38cm (15 inches) and is easily identified when seen at its roost by its dark eyes which lack the yellow eye ring typical of all other British owls except the white barn owl (*Tyto alba*). It chooses to nest in hollow trees or under the eroded roots, and it would be even more common if park authorities were to leave old trees standing, even though dead, which make wonderful refuges both for owls and woodpeckers. The little owl (*Athene noctua*) was introduced into Britain from Holland in the 1870s and has successfully spread since. At 22cm (8½ inches) this small owl does not

The treecreeper's down-curved bill is perfect for removing insects from bark.

disaster befalls the first brood a repeat clutch is sometimes attempted, but the species is usually single-brooded.

In some parks nest-boxes for great tits, blue tits and spotted flycatchers have proved popular. Sometimes the entrance holes are found to have been enlarged, and the gnawing teeth of the grey squirrel are often blamed. However, great spotted woodpeckers are the real culprits and a substantial part of their summer diet consists of fledgling birds and eggs. It is no wonder that the tiny mouse-like treecreeper goes to such pains to hide its nest behind the flaking bark of a plane or birch.

Grey squirrel.

**Above** Green-veined white.

**Below** Female cabbage white.

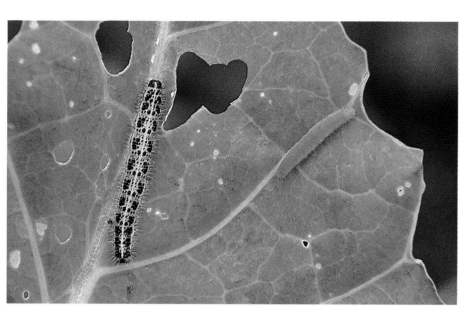

compete for food with the larger tawny and feeds mainly upon insects. It does, however, have to take care in order to avoid falling victim to the tawny owl, which finds a little owl a tasty meal. Little owls do take a few small birds, but perhaps the greatest threat to these species, especially during the breeding season, is the grey squirrel.

Large white and small white caterpillars.

## Grey squirrel Sciurus carolinensis

The Handbook of British Mammals points out that the grey squirrel is a 'controversial mammal regarded by many as a disastrous pest but by some town dwellers as an attractive asset'. There is a suggestion that the grey squirrel was present in North Wales in 1830, but there is no doubt that the bulk of the introductions from North America were made between 1876 and 1929 at places as far apart as Henbury, Cheshire (1876), Bushey, Middlesex (1889), Loch Long, Scotland (1896), Lyme, Cheshire (1903), Kew Gardens, London (1908), Birmingham (1912), Exeter (1915) and Edinburgh (1921). By 1930 the species was recognised as more of a problem

than the native red squirrel (Sciurus vulgaris), which has never really adapted to urban living. By 1940, when it had recovered from a temporary set-back due to a virus disease, the grey squirrel was recognised as a serious pest in many areas, including London, and an unrelenting battle was waged against the newcomer, which had moved into a comfortable ecological niche containing no natural predator. It is now illegal to keep or import grey squirrels without a licence from the Ministry of Agriculture or the Secretary of State for Scotland.

There is no doubt that the feeding habits of the grey squirrel can cause havoc in urban parkland. During the winter months they eat bark and many trees are killed by squirrels 'ringing' the tree and preventing the movement of water and food up and down the trunk. Their habit of eating eggs and young birds and a tendency to nip off the succulent tips of sap-filled spring buds are also very frustrating for those trying to develop nature trails in urban parks. But there can be no doubt about the popularity of squirrels with visitors, who eagerly offer them scraps and nuts and excitedly point out their antics among the boughs of the trees.

An adult grey squirrel weighs about 520g (18 ounces) and its body measures 26cm (8 inches). Contrary to popular opinion squirrels do not hibernate and, indeed, are at their most active during February days when the ground is covered in snow. It is at this time that their breeding occurs. The only thing which keeps them within their twiggy drey set in the fork of a tree is a high wind, since they are unable to judge distance when branches are violently gusting about. Female grey squirrels usually begin to breed when they are one year old and can produce two litters each year after a forty-three day gestation period. As many as six young are produced in each litter, which explains why populations increase rapidly and have to be controlled. What *is* wrong is to view them as disease-ridden tree rats which need exterminating. Rather, they should be regarded as beautiful creatures which are too numerous and need controlling. We should also remember that we ourselves originally introduced squirrels to Britain to increase the delights of our wildlife. If only we had taken the time to look into the undergrowth of our parks we would have found enough beauty there to satisfy our needs.

## The undergrowth

Park authorities have much the same attitude to undergrowth as they do to decaying trees. I once pleaded the case for a wild corner with a park-keeper who told me brusquely that it would attract insects. It certainly would. There is nothing like a good patch of nettles to attract butterflies, the most innocent of our insects yet the group that has suffered more than any other. In 1984, the official 'Year of the Butterfly', butterfly farms did a roaring trade selling eggs to well-meaning folk intending to re-introduce them into areas where butterflies are absent. This admirable intention can only be realised if the correct plants are available for the caterpillars to feed upon.

A fascinating project for a naturalists' group or for a school close to a park or able to set aside a wild area on the playing fields is to create a habitat where butterflies can breed. First of all you need to sow the right plants, then once they are established introduce butterflies at the time when their food is at its best. The wall brown (*Lasiommata megera*) requires couch grasses or twitch (*Agropyron* spp) and foxtails (*Alopecurus* spp), which would present no problem if only the authorities did not hate them so much and would desist from trying to eradicate them with gallons of herbicide.

The green-veined white (*Pieris napi*) is unfortunate in that it is regularly accused of gobbling up cabbages simply because it happens to be white and so is bracketed with the large white (*Pieris brassicae*), whose caterpillars do eat cabbage and are a nuisance. The green-veined white's caterpillars in fact feed on members of the cress family, especially lady's smock (*Cardamine pratensis*), as well as aubretia. In encouraging butterflies it should not be forgotten that, whilst the adults do not live long and do not increase in size, they do require fuel for flight. The green-veined white, for example, requires a good supply of hawthorn flowers or hawkbit (*Leontodon* spp) to provide energy-rich nectar.

As far as municipal parks are concerned, planning a come-back for butterflies may not be such a simple matter and it may well be that most parks prefer to begin with a less ambitious programme involving the small tortoiseshell (*Aglais urticae*) and the peacock (*Inachis io*), two very attractive species that require common stinging nettles for the caterpillars and dandelions and bramble for the adults. Leaving large areas of dandelion and nettle would no doubt expose park authorities

Wall brown – a woodland butterfly now adapted to life in town parks.

*Cyclops*, the whirligig beetle (*Gyrinus*) and the fish louse (*Argulus*), which is often found adhering to the body of the three-spined stickleback (*Gasterosteus aculeatus*), one of the most fascinating of all fish.

We quite rightly praise the salmon for having the complex chemistry required to move slowly from the sea into fresh water to breed and the eel for travelling in the reverse

to criticism, but what about the areas behind the nursery greenhouses, or, even better, the hollows on the islands in park lakes? These would provide an ideal open-air laboratory where amateur groups could work with park authorities to create butterfly gardens.

## Park lakes

The lakes themselves, so popular with anglers and with duck and swan feeders, should never be despised by urban naturalists. To begin a study of the wildlife that thrives there we could do worse than peep into a young fisherman's jam-jar. If it is held up to the light, hundreds of tiny water fleas belonging to the family *Daphnidae* will be seen swimming about with jerky movements. When placed under a low-power microscope their transparent beauty can be seen, including the beating of the heart and the movement of food through the gut. Many first-class microscopists have learned their trade by dabbling in park lakes, which because of their recreational function are kept free from pollution and teem with small plants (phytoplankton) and invertebrates. Among the invertebrates found there are the one-eyed crustacean

**Above** Water flea (*Daphnia*).

**Below** Fish louse (*Argulus coregoni*).

**Above** Moorhen in its normal garb.　　　　**Below** Coot on nest.

direction, but we pay no attention to the 'tiddler' in the park lake. If the urban stickleback is taken to the coast and dumped in the sea, it is able to adjust immediately; indeed, sticklebacks have been found as far as six miles out to sea. Neither the salmon or the eel can adjust as quickly as the humble stickleback.

## The breeding cycle of the three-spined stickleback

As the breeding season approaches, the male stickleback loses his undistinguished yellow-brown colour, his belly turns red, his dorsal surface darkens and his eyes become highlighted by circles of brilliant blue. He is now ready to repel other males from his territory and attract plump females loaded with eggs into his domain. Both these aspects of behaviour can be triggered by presenting the aggressive male fish with a series of models. Anything red is violently buffeted and a shape looking even remotely like a fat female is treated to a sinuous zigzag dance. If she is ready to lay her eggs, the female dances with the gaudy male and follows him into a tunnel-like nest he has constructed from bits of weed cemented together with a secretion from his kidneys. This secretion may well contain a chemical that stimulates the female to lay her clutch of between 100 and 400 eggs which the male, following behind, fertilises.

A successful male may persuade several females to leave eggs in his charge. They are safe in his care because he maintains a flow of oxygen over them by carrying out a fanning action with his fins. Once they hatch he continues to defend his offspring and he is certainly not guilty of eating them, although he is sometimes accused of doing so. When danger threatens he sucks the young into his mouth, only to puff them out again when it is safe.

Systematic studies of the aquatic life of a town lake have seldom been attempted and would well repay the efforts of a naturalists' group.

## The bird life of park lakes

Regular surveys of bird life around a boating lake always reveal a surprising variety of birds living at peace with the rowing and paddle boats. It is easy to see why birds such as moorhens, coots and dabchicks are happy on park boating lakes, for there are many shallow areas where they are well out of reach of oars and paddles – and, since the pleasure boats do not operate in winter or at night and there are plenty of wet and windy days during the summer when the boats are not used at all, for most of the time the birds are left to themselves.

### Moorhen *Gallinula chloropus*

About 300,000 pairs of moorhens breed in Britain. The plumage of this delightful member of the rail family is dark brown with contrasting white stripes on the flanks and a red frontal shield on the bill, which has a bright yellow tip. The white undertail coverts are separated by a black line and the pattern shows up clearly as the moorhen swims in its typically jerky manner. Occasionally albino moorhens occur. Their lack of camouflage makes them vulnerable, but they stand a better chance of surviving in the protected environment of a park lake than in the wild, where they are at the mercy of predators such as mink. In a parkland situation the moorhen is itself something of a predator, the eggs and young of small birds making a nutritious addition to its normal diet of snails, tadpoles and fish. Early in the morning, especially after rain, moorhens may be seen on the grassy areas of the park feeding on earthworms flushed from their burrows.

The nest of the moorhen, which is built by both sexes from dead reeds, is usually concealed in vegetation overhanging the water. But this is by no means the only site available in parkland and nests are often found hidden among rhododendron bushes. The size of the clutch may vary from as few as two eggs to a staggering twenty or more, though these

Albino moorhen.

large clutches are doubtless due to two females laying in the same nest. The eggs, which are buff-coloured and spotted and blotched with rusty-red, are incubated by both parents for about three weeks. After leaving the nest at three days the young are fed by both parents; they are self-sufficient in about five weeks. Two and sometimes three broods are reared in a season, the parents' task being made easier by the young from the earlier broods assisting in the feeding.

## Coot *Fulica atra*

At 37cm (15 inches) the coot is a full 5cm (2 inches) larger than the moorhen and is much more aggressive. The coot dives for its food, which consists of water weed as well as fish and aquatic crustaceans and insects. It does not, therefore, compete with the moorhen. Many species found on park lakes obtain their food by diving, and each has its own technique. The dive of the coot involves a distinct jump to build up momentum before submerging.

Where the population is high, coots may nest semi-colonially, but on most park lakes nests are usually solitary and are built of dead leaves. In a Manchester park, however, I watched a coot build its nest from ice-cream cartons, crisp packets and saturated pages of the *Evening News*. Both parents incubate the clutch of from five to fifteen buff eggs, spotted lightly with black, for just over three weeks and both feed the young, which are independent in about two months. The breeding season can begin as early as March and the last clutch of young may not fly until mid-November, which gives ample time for three broods to be raised. One pair in a Nottingham park produced a clutch of eggs as late as November.

An adult coot with its dark plumage and

Little grebe or dabchick.

white frontal shield (or 'bald spot') and bill is easily recognised, but the small brownish young are less distinctive. As a result, little grebes, which often breed on urban park lakes, are sometimes not recognised as a separate species and are mistakenly recorded as the young of either coots or moorhens.

## Little grebe *Podiceps ruficollis*

The little grebe – also known as the dabchick, an attractive alternative name for this 25cm (10 inches) bundle of energy – is the smallest of the European grebes. Britain has between 10,000 and 20,000 breeding pairs. The dabchick is the only grebe completely without any ornamentation on its head during the breeding season, though the rich brown plumage and the reddish cheeks, throat and

neck are quite distinctive in summer. The winter plumage is much paler.

During the winter the British resident populations of little grebe, coot and moorhen are swelled considerably by visitors from northern Europe driven south and west by the harsher northern winters. The urban park lakes, with their resident birds active early in the morning before human activities begin, attract the migrating birds, which are often following the line of a river valley, and down they come into what is virtually a bird sanctuary. The increasing tendency of local authorities to keep pinioned wildfowl such as Canada geese in their parks, a practice begun by Charles II in St James's Park as long ago as 1670, also attracts wild tufted duck, smew, pochard, mallard, goldeneye and even the occasional herd of whooper swans into the heart of the city.

# 5 Gardens

Many years ago, as a biology student in London, I was invited to visit the home of my elderly cleaning lady. When I mentioned that I was studying the techniques of setting up a nature reserve, she lost no time in taking me into her tiny walled garden and pointed out that if all the small plots in our cities were added together they would amount to the greatest nature reserve in the land. I have never forgotten that lesson, which is even truer today now that more houses have gardens than ever before and gardening has become something of a national obsession. Most gardeners, however, especially in towns, tend to think that a neat and tidy garden is essential. Rarely now do you find cascades of cottage garden flowers, buzzing with bees, flashing with the colourful wings of butterflies and heavy with rich perfume. Out have gone perfumed lavender and sweet william and in have come bright bedding plants bred by the garden centres for size and colour, with less regard for the scent and nectar loved by the insects which pollinate them. Several books have been published recently about wild or scented gardens. As a result, a small minority of gardeners now grow wild flowers. Nevertheless, the idea of having a wild corner full of weeds for wildlife does not often dawn upon the average gardener, armed with a formidable array of weedkillers and insecticides. However, a weed is merely a plant growing where it is not wanted – so, by definition, if you want a few nettles tucked away in a corner, then they are not weeds.

There are many houses in the cities which have large gardens – some well maintained, but others magnificent jungles. Both badgers

(*Meles meles*) and the red fox (*Vulpes vulpes*) thrive in such places. Indeed, the fox is fast becoming as much an urban animal as a beast of the country.

Much more numerous, however, are the smaller 'town gardens' and it is the purpose of this chapter to indicate how these can be managed for wildlife and how the creatures living in them may be studied. With a little planning and a lot of work it is possible to have five study areas – a border hedge, soil, flowers and fruit bushes, even if in tubs, a small pond and a cat-proof bird-table.

## The border hedge

### Privet *Ligustrum vulgare*

Privet is a slow-growing deciduous shrub which can grow to as much as 5m (16 feet) in height. It is native to Britain and therefore supports a wide range of interesting insects. It has been used as a hedging plant and as a substitute for walls for centuries and is widely distributed throughout Europe, apart from the far north, eastern Asia and New Guinea, and is even found in Queensland, Australia. There are more exotic species, including the golden privet (*Ligustrum ovalifolium*) introduced from Japan and bearing panicles of fragrant cream-coloured flowers. Golden privet does not fare well in industrialised areas, however, and the urban naturalist-gardener is better off with the native species, which provides food for the caterpillar of one of Britain's most beautiful moths.

### Privet hawk moth *Sphinx ligustri*

The caterpillar of the privet hawk moth feeds not only on privet but also on lilac – a complex of introduced species which originated in China and Central Europe. The most common species is *Syringa vulgaris*, which not only has a delightful smell but also copes well with urban atmospheres. A combination of privet and lilac should ensure a visit from the privet hawk moth in southern England. The moth is rarer in the north, though I have photographed the species on privet in Manchester and on lilac in Blackburn and have also seen it as far north as Carlisle.

The adult moth, which emerges from its brown chrysalis deep in the soil during June, is a magnificent insect, with a wingspan of 12·5cm (almost 5 inches). The abdomen is flushed with a delicate pink and is barred with black, broken down the centre by a wide buff-coloured line. The two pairs of scaly wings, typical of the Lepidoptera, are pale brown mottled with darker brown, white and pink. Throughout July and August the adults feed on the rich nectar offered by late-flowering lilac and privet, on which the eggs are laid. The time taken for the eggs to hatch varies with temperature, but when the caterpillars are mature they measure fully 7·5cm (3 inches). They are recognisable as a member of the hawk moth genus by the hook-like structure at the tip of the abdomen but are distinguished from other hawk moths by the seven purple and white stripes which run obliquely along the side of the translucent body. When ready to pupate, the caterpillar burrows up to 20cm (8 inches) into the ground below the food plant, before changing into the pupa (chrysalis) inside which the metamorphosis to the adult moth takes place.

It is at this stage that the conservation-minded naturalist-photographer can have great fun by collecting the chrysalides and waiting for the adults to emerge. Until the wings are dry the insect is immobile and can be easily photographed. By collecting the chrysalides the moths are protected from hungry birds until their wings are fully functional. There are, however, much more subtle enemies lying in wait, especially for the caterpillars during their succulent later stages. Not least amongst these are the ichneumons, one of the least understood groups of parasites.

## Ichneumons

The ichneumons are closely related to wasps. The generally dull-coloured adults have long narrow bodies and long sensitive antennae, with which the males locate mates and the females scent their prey. The most frequent

Privet hawk moth adult.

Ichneumon fly.

Privet hawk moth larva.

victims are insect larvae, especially those of butterflies, moths and hoverflies. Little work had been done on hoverflies until recently, but Dr Jennifer Owen, working in her town garden in Leicester, caught 529 species in three years, beginning in 1971 – that is more than 25 per cent of all British species. Of these, eight were species new to Britain and two had never previously been described. Such painstaking research is not easy but it does show that, wherever you live, a garden can be an outdoor laboratory if you care to use it as such. Identification of individual ichneumon species is difficult, but if, through naturalists' groups, interested amateurs are put in touch with experts able to help with identification, that has the twin advantage of adding to the amateur's knowledge, while the expert gains help in plotting species distribution. The best way to obtain ichneumons is to collect larvae containing the grubs of the parasite and to wait for the adults to emerge.

A common species of ichneumon that surprisingly has no common name is *Apanteles glomeratus*, which attacks the larvae of large white butterflies. The female parasite has a long, pointed ovipositor adapted from the hymenopteran sting and with this she stabs into the tissues of the caterpillar, taking great care to miss its vital organs. As many as 100 eggs are laid in a single grub (although some of the larger species may lay only one) and these hatch into larvae which eat away the inside of the caterpillar, eventually killing it and leaving it as an empty shell. The ichneumons then pupate inside their tiny yellow cocoons before emerging the following year as mature adults, ready to breed and continue the life-cycle.

*Apanteles* is very common and does as much, probably more, to protect our cabbages from the attentions of the large white as all the chemicals used by gardeners. These usually destroy the ichneumons as well as the pests – a most wasteful practice, apart from the conservational ethics involved. Indeed, it is arguable that ichneumons are more effective than chemicals and they would be able to render Britain's large white butterflies (*Pieris brassicae*) extinct unaided, were it not for the large numbers which reach us from the Continent each summer.

Another ichneumon commonly found in gardens in *Coccygomius instigator*, which is often attracted to artificial light. It is typified by a dark body and red legs, the tips of the third pair of which are also black. This species parasitises the snout moth (*Hypena proboscidalis*), which is a brownish species, with the forewings and body darker than the hind wings and a forewing span of almost 4cm (about 1³/₅ inches). It has a pointed head and its so-called 'snout' is formed from the swollen feeding palps around the mouth. The larvae are to be found feeding on nettles and it is here that the ichneumons seek them out.

Dr Jennifer Owen found that moth larvae collected from her flowering currant bushes, especially magpie moth larvae, acted as hosts to several species of ichneumon. Dr Owen makes the point that even introduced species (flowering currants come from North America) are surprisingly quickly adopted by native fauna and even the most exotically tropical-looking garden can be rich in wildlife. I once had a student who imaginatively chose the fauna of a gooseberry bush as the subject of her thesis and identified a number of ichneumons from the hollow parasitised bodies of magpie moth larvae.

## Magpie moth *Abraxas grossulariata*

This attractive species, on the wing during the summer and occasionally hibernating as an adult during the winter, is easily recognised by its striking colours. Although they show a great deal of variation, the magpie moth's basic combination of yellow, orange and black spots and blotches contrasts sharply with the

**Above** The woolly-bear caterpillar of the garden tiger moth.

**Below** Caterpillar of the magpie moth.

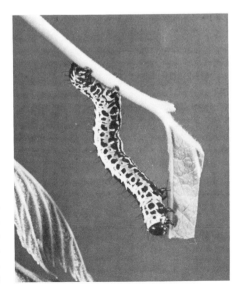

dunnock, all of which eagerly consume the larvae of the magpie moth and other destructive insects. Thus a winter bird-table that attracts local birds into your garden can be an important prelude to protecting summer fruit.

## Soil

Although your skill as a gardener and the position of your garden have some bearing, it is above all the chemical make-up of the soil that determines which plants will grow – and

Garden tiger moth.

Magpie moth.

white ground colour of the wings. The moths lay their eggs on the leaves of currant or gooseberry bushes, so the gardener should welcome the ichneumons which lay their eggs in the beautiful larvae. The larvae have the same basic colours as the adult moths and usually hibernate on a twig of a tree. The species is widely distributed throughout Britain and I have even found it in the Outer Hebrides feeding on ling. The versatile larvae also feed on apple, hawthorn, sloe, elm and navelwort (*Cotyledon umbelicus*).

In addition to the ichneumons, the gardener should also welcome birds such as the song thrush, robin, wren, blackbird and

the plants and the soil in turn decide which animals are attracted to your garden. Snails, for example, cannot live in lime-free soil because they require calcium salts to build their shells and earthworms find it impossible to burrow in waterlogged clay soil. Gardeners can, therefore, profoundly affect the wildlife in a garden by the mere act of digging, apart from any attempt to achieve a balance between wet clay soil on the one hand and sandy lime-deficient soil on the other.

### Earthworms

Some idea of the health of a garden's soil can be gained by counting the earthworm popu-

Mouth

Rounded anterior region

32

37

Clitellum (also called the saddle)

Flattened posterior region

Anus

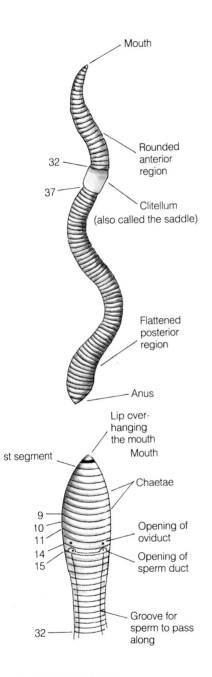

Lip over-hanging the mouth

Mouth

st segment

Chaetae

9
10
11

Opening of oviduct

14
15

Opening of sperm duct

32

Groove for sperm to pass along

Anatomy of earthworm.

Nematodes.

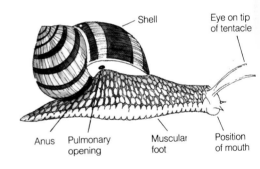

Shell

Eye on tip of tentacle

Anus   Pulmonary opening

Muscular foot

Position of mouth

External features of snail (**above**) and slug (**below**).

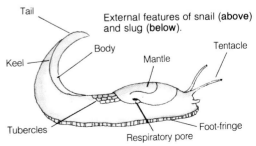

Tail

Keel

Body

Mantle

Tentacle

Tubercles

Respiratory pore

Foot-fringe

lation. Choose a rainy day and mark out with string one square metre (just over a yard). Onto the marked area pour a dilute solution (about 15 grams to 4 litres of water, or ½ ounce to 1 gallon) of potassium permanganate. Some worms remain below but a surprising number come to the surface and can be counted. In Britain we have twenty-five species of earthworm, but only nine are at all common in gardens and different species have distinct habitat preferences, some being found in sand and others in heavier soils.

To most gardeners a worm is just a worm but, although the basic structure is similar in all earthworms, there are easily observed differences for those who take the time to look. Aristotle called earthworms the intestines of the earth; they have also been described as humus factories with bodies like steel. These descriptions are extremely apt, since earthworms push, twist and eat their way through the soil assisted by a system of bristles called setae (or chaetae) which grip the soil. The strength of these – there are usually two pairs per segment – can be seen if you watch a bird trying to extract a reluctant earthworm from its burrow. The segments on the earthworm's body are clearly visible and are responsible for the phylum name of Annelida which derives from the Latin *anellus*, a ring. The number of these ring-like segments varies from about 150 to 400, depending on the species.

The brandling (*Eisenia foetida*) is a comparatively small worm, usually less than 15cm (6 inches) long. It is very common in manure and compost heaps – indeed, it is also known as the manure worm or stinking earthworm. When crushed it has a most disagreeable smell and it probably does not taste very nice either, which may account for the fact that birds tend to ignore it in favour of the more pleasant-tasting species such as the common earthworm (*Lumbricus terrestris*), otherwise known as the rain worm. As it crawls around in the wet soil the bright pinky violet colour of this worm is often hidden by mud. When mature it may be up to 30cm (12 inches) long and birds find it irresistible.

Another common garden species is *Lumbricus rubellus*. It is favoured by anglers since fish not only like the species but are attracted by its bright red colour. The garden spade is also likely to unearth *Allolobophora longa*, a brown species, and *Allolobophora chlorotica*, which is green, whilst *Lumbricus castoneus* is a small worm about 3·75cm (1½ inches) long with a bright orange saddle. *Octolasium lacteum* also has an orange saddle, but is otherwise bluish in colour, whilst *Octolasium cyaneum* is also bluish with a red saddle and yellow posterior segments. When handled this species gives off a thick milky fluid, which may well serve to deter birds. All of these species are commonly found in town gardens.

An interesting project is to learn to identify the various species of earthworm, collect a number of each species, place them at random on a bird-table and note which the birds prefer.

## Nematodes

It has been estimated that the top 15cm of a square metre of soil might contain as many as twenty million nematodes, otherwise known as roundworms. In terms of numbers they must be among the most successful creatures on earth. Nematodes are unsegmented and occur in every habitat. Many species are parasites, including *Ascaris* (the pinworm), common in man, and the dreaded *Filaria*, which infests the lymph glands and causes the tropical disease elephantiasis. A particularly fascinating species found in gardens is known as the thunderworm (*Mermis*), which looks like a thin piece of string and is often as much as 50cm (20 inches) long. The name relates to its tendency to emerge onto the soaking ground during a thunderstorm. However, it cannot live in dry conditions and soon slinks away in search of moisture when the soil is dry. The adults do no damage but the young bore into the bodies of insects, especially beetles, to feed on the tissues. Some nematodes can infect pests and are therefore of value to the gardener, though some can be a nuisance.

The nematodes which gardeners really fear are the eelworms. These creatures, usually quite tiny, do a great deal of damage to the plant roots on which they feed. The potato eelworm can damage potato roots so badly that the crop fails completely. Most horrifying of all is the ability of eelworm eggs to survive for long periods inside drought-resistant cysts from which they hatch when suitable conditions return, ready to infest subsequent crops.

## Slugs and snails

The phylum Mollusca comprises about 110,000 species. All are distinguished by the division of their bodies into three basic parts: head, foot and a hump-like mass often covered by a shell. The phylum is divided into three classes: the Cephalopods, made up of squids and octopuses; the Lamellibranchiata or bivalves, so-called because their shells are in two halves; and the mainly land-based Gastropods, to which both snails and slugs belong. These both prefer damp, lush vegetation and feed on plant leaves, which makes them a pest in the garden. They also eat a lot of humus, which they grind up using a rasp-like structure called the radula. Land snails are hermaphrodite and have a unique and bizarre method of reproduction. The two mating snails lie side by side and exchange sperm, with which they fertilise their eggs, by each thrusting a sharp, chalky protruberance into the other's flank. Newborn snails possess tiny shells, which are enlarged year by year to accommodate the increasing body size. No growth occurs in the winter, when snails hibernate under a stone or in a crevice in a wall.

## Common snail *Helix aspersa*

The overall body colour of the common or garden snail is dark grey, and the even darker shell is attractively speckled with grey and yellow. This snail is not often found in industrial areas where smoke has obviously affected its food plants. As the Clean Air Acts have improved the environment *Helix aspersa* has once more become common in some urban areas. The Roman or edible snail (*Helix pomatia*) occurs on downlands and not in gardens, except when it is deliberately kept for the table, but the garden snail is equally palatable and not very long ago was an important item in the Englishman's diet.

## Hairy snail *Trichia hispida*

The hairy snail is covered with a layer of fine hairs which makes the shell appear dull. It is generally accepted that the hairs serve to anchor the snail under stones, walls or logs, making it harder for birds or other predators to remove it. I wonder if the hairs may have a second function. I have noticed that the species seems able to exist in drier places than some other snails and it may be that the hairs also cut down water loss. Sometimes the hairs get scraped off and the lovely brown shell can then be seen glistening in the sun like beaten copper. The hairy snail is common throughout Britain. It feeds on plants, but is not such a pest as the strawberry snail (*Hygromia striolata*) which, as its name implies, can play havoc with strawberry beds. Young strawberry snails also tend to be hairy, but lose their hairs with age. The species occurs throughout England and Wales and as far north as Pitlochry in Scotland.

## Glass snails

Two species of glass snails are encountered in urban gardens. The cellar glass snail (*Oxychilus cellarius*) has a flattened, almost transparent yellowish-brown shell with a white centre portion called the umbellicus. It is quite a small species, measuring only 5mm wide by 10mm high ($\frac{1}{5} \times \frac{2}{5}$ inch). It is found in damp places in and around the garden, being particularly attracted to garden sheds and cellars. It also has a most unpleasant smell. The garlic glass snail (*Oxychilus alliarius*) gets its name from its aroma. Its shell measures 2·5mm high by 6·5mm wide ($^1/_{10}$ × $^1/_4$ inch) and is blue-black and even glossier than that of the cellar glass snail.

## Slugs

The most common species in the garden is probably the pale cream netted slug (*Agriolimax reticulatus*), which is richly blotched with warm brown. The garden slug (*Arion hortensis*) can easily be recognised by the orange sole of its foot, which also has a prominent groove running round its edge. The great grey slug (*Limax maximus*) has a keel down the rear third of its back and when fully grown can reach 20cm (8 inches) in length.

Although slugs do not differ from snails in their basic biological functions, they have lost most, if not all, of the shell and the area under it, called the visceral hump, containing the body organs. This means they have greater difficulty in coping with water loss and have packed their body organs into the foot. There are about twenty-four British species, divided into three groups: the shelled, the keeled and the round-backed slugs. The three species of shelled slugs are characterised by a tiny remnant of shell. The most likely to be seen in the urban garden is *Testacella haliotidae*, the common shelled slug, which is not easy to find because it spends its time burrowing in search of earthworms – its main food item.

The keeled slugs are obviously typified by the possession of a keel. The best example is *Limax maximus*, which is particularly common in gardens as well as in cellars and outhouses. The mating behaviour is remarkable, even for a mollusc: the pair climb a bush or other suitable object, from which they suspend themselves on a thick twine of mucus before each piercing the other's body with a sharp spine containing sperm. The netted slug is also a keeled type, but the large grey-black

slug (*Limax cinereoniger*) is an example of the round-backed group. It can approach 30cm (12 inches) in size, but is very rare in urban gardens and was probably more common in Britain's ancient woodlands.

Slugs are, in fact, not always quite so harmful as their reputation suggests and prefer to scavenge on more easily digestible rotting vegetation than on tougher, fresher material. For this reason the tidy gardener, who sweeps litter from paths and leaves from lawns and picks the withered foliage from his green vegetables, is more likely to suffer from the activities of slugs. Deprived of their preferred food, slugs turn to the only alternative – fresh green crops. Molluscs are also the only animal group capable of digesting cellulose.

## Plants for wildlife

By careful planting a naturalist-gardener can do a great deal to add to his garden the colour, interest and above all surprises that wildlife has to offer. Two kinds of plants are needed. Firstly, exotic, colourful and perhaps non-native plants to give food and cover; and secondly, a wild corner of native plants likely to prove attractive to native fauna.

### Cotoneaster

There are fifty species of cotoneaster, which is a member of the rose family, some deciduous, others evergreen. Some are low arching shrubs but others are quite tall, growing up to 4m (13 feet). The family is made even more complicated by the fact that the species interbreed. The clusters of five-petalled flowers are white or pink, but it is the red, or occasionally black, berries that are the real bonus for wildlife and can attract rare birds, such as the waxwing, into the urban garden. The two most common planted species are the evergreen *Cotoneaster franchettii* and the deciduous *Cotoneaster horizontalis*. When both are planted, berries are found at all heights and the branches provide ideal perches for birds. Although it is uncommon in the wild, cotoneaster is an indigenous plant of the Northern hemisphere and is therefore attractive to our own wild birds and birds from other parts of Europe.

## Waxwing *Bombycilla garrulus*

This plump, colourful bird is easily recognised by its pinkish-brown upper plumage and much paler feathering below. The bird owes its name to the wax-red tips of its upper flight feathers. The black throat and eye line stand out clearly, as does the broad yellow tip of the tail. The crest is a most attractive feature of these 15cm (7 inch) birds and to see them feeding in the garden is a delight. It is a pity that they are so uncommon – indeed, in some years they do not appear in Britain at all. The waxwing's normal habitat is northern Europe and so long as the berry crop can support the population they remain in the breeding area. Should the berry crop there fail, the hungry birds irrupt in all directions and some turn up in Britain to feed greedily on the fruits of rowan, hawthorn and rose, and gobble up the cotoneaster berries in even the smallest of gardens. Waxwings are very gregarious and winter irruptions were recorded even before bird movements were considered to be of interest. In 1679–80 there was a large influx; irruptions were also recorded in 1830–1, 1834–5, 1849–50, 1866–7 and 1930–1; and in 1965–6 a huge immigration occurred, when more than 11,000 poured into Britain.

One plant that attracts waxwings is the firethorn (*Pyracantha coccinea*), a member of the rose family native to Turkey and southern Europe with sharp, spiny thorns which provides not only food but, equally important, cover for suitable breeding sites.

Red admiral butterfly feeding on wind-fall pears.

## Plants to attract butterflies

Waxwing resting in a town centre tree.

The three plants most likely to entice butterflies into your garden are buddleia, ice plant and marjoram. Indeed, *Buddleia davidii* is so attractive to Lepidoptera that it is also known as the 'butterfly bush'. During its flowering period in July and August its nectar attracts small tortoiseshells, peacocks, large and small whites, and the splendid red admiral. The presence of marjoram (*Origanum vulgare*) adds to populations and if ice plant (*Sedum spectabile*) is also present the supply of nectar is kept on tap until September. Stone-crops, lavenders, Michaelmas daisies, thymes, petunias and tobacco plants are all attractive species popular both with diurnal and nocturnal moths. Red admirals are much more numerous in some years than others, but gardens with old-fashioned flower borders are

most likely to attract them. If there is an ivy-clad wall, red admirals may survive on the wing until November.

## Red admiral *Vanessa atalanta*

The red admiral can never be a year-round resident in Britain because at no stage in its life-cycle is it capable of surviving the rigours of a cold winter, though a few adults may hang on throughout the winter if the season is milder than usual. However, immigration from the Continent can begin as early as February and some butterflies of this species may be truly migratory. The eggs are laid, usually in June, on nettle leaves. Gardeners who plant species to attract butterflies yet refuse to allow a single nettle to grow miss the opportunity of helping the population to increase. When it is ready to pupate, the black caterpillar constructs a tent-like structure out of silk from which the adult butterfly emerges, unless the caterpillar has been attacked by an ichneumon. Usually the red admiral is single-brooded and in autumn the adults enjoy idling in the sun and sucking the juice from rotting fruit, the red and white wing patches standing out clearly against their velvety black wings. Tidy gardeners who pick up windfalls deprive themselves of the pleasure of watching these attractive drinking parties.

## The wild corner

Any garden without nettles is a disaster for wildlife. If you are not keen on the idea of letting nettles roam at large in your garden, you can cordon off a wild corner and even label it as such. The original home of the nettle was woodland and it was once harvested as a crop and eaten, boiled, as a vegetable. It was also converted into cloth as early as the Bronze Age, or before. It was still used for this purpose in some parts of Scotland until the eighteenth century and German army uniforms during the First World War contained nettle fibre. Surprisingly, in the days when the plant was cultivated as a crop for food and clothing, before fertilisers were available, it was difficult to grow, since nettles demand a high nitrogen content in the soil. Other butterflies as well as the red admiral depend on nettles to nourish their larvae, including the peacock and the small tortoiseshell.

**Above** Peacock butterfly larva.

**Below** Larva of small tortoiseshell butterfly.

### Peacock *Inachis io*

This species is on the wing from July until October and the adults drink nectar from marjoram, clover, knapweed and thistle. The single brood of eggs is laid in large batches piled in the form of a pyramid on the underside of nettles – the only food plant which peacock larvae will accept. Peacock larvae are almost black but dotted with flecks of white which distinguish them from the larvae of the tinier small tortoiseshell. The pupae may be either light green, tinged with orange, or khaki. What determines these differences is not known. The gregarious larvae seem to react to a common signal and all march off to hang upside-down to pupate. The adults emerge during August and go into hiber-

**Above** Peacock butterflies feeding on sedum.　**Below** Small tortoiseshell butterfly.

nation during October, emerging again in the warm sunshine of April or even earlier in a good spring.

## Small tortoiseshell *Aglais urticae*

The larvae of this butterfly also require nettles for food. The species seems to have favourite breeding areas, and will soon adapt and treat your wild corner as home. Some trimming may be of assistance, since small tortoiseshell females always choose shorter patches of nettle and will be attracted to trimmed sections. The eggs are laid in a mass near the top of a young nettle plant. Until just before pupation the larvae are gregarious. Groups cover themselves with a protective tent of silk, but pupate singly at some distance from the food plant. They hang by the tail end from the eaves of houses or from fences or window-sills. Adults emerge from the pupae around September and it is the adult which hibernates. The ice plant is a favourite nectar supply, but small tortoiseshells are also attracted to Michaelmas daisy and buddleia. There is some evidence that the British population is augmented by Continental immigrants.

The wild corner should not be maintained only for animals but also for the plants in their own right. Douglas Davis (*Country-Side*, summer 1982) had this to say about his own patch: 'This corner is waist high in nettles and docks; a bramble grows against the old brick wall that runs the length of the patch, ivy hangs over the wall, and white bryony trails over the decrepit shed, its hand-like leaves and greenish white blossom weaving over the heaps of coal inside, where it has penetrated the cracks in the worm-eaten planking. I like it.'

So do I. A little thought plus the avoidance of the use of harmful chemicals can convert

Common frog.

any garden into a wildlife sanctuary. Wild plants will quickly appear, their seeds carried on the wind or on the feet of birds. Douglas Davis noted the presence of 'ragwort, dandelion, daisy, stinging nettle and dead nettles, both greater and lesser bindweed, shepherd's purse, cleavers (goosegrass), field speedwell, goosefoot, wood spurge, field pansy, pineapple weed, garlic mustard, fumitory, nipplewort and comfrey'. Altogether forty-six plants were listed. It is now possible to buy packets of seeds from a number of firms, which have increased their business since the Wildlife and Countryside Act made it illegal to uproot wild flowers.

# The garden pond

The number of plants and animals can be increased by the provision of a garden pond, however small. Garden centres, nowadays a boom industry in Britain, offer many shapes and sizes of premoulded garden pond. In fact, an old sink serves just as well and I would prefer several small ponds to one large one. British amphibians – we only have six – are struggling for survival at the moment. Three of these breed happily in a garden pond: namely the common frog, the common toad and the smooth newt.

## Common frog *Rana temporaria*

The problems encountered by this once abundant species have already been described, and garden ponds are important for securing its future. Care should be taken not to have trees overhanging the pond, since shade can prevent the growth of aquatic plants. The pond should not be of even depth and needs to have an area shallow enough for young amphibians to reach dry land.

Mature frogs return to breeding ponds during March. The females are larger than the males, which are recognised by the black horny pads on their thumbs used to grip the female. A male may hang on to the back of a female for several days, fertilising the eggs as

they are laid. The eggs are surrounded by a jelly which holds them together and protects them from predators as well as from physical injury. The jelly may also contain a chemical which prevents attack by fungi and bacteria. The time the eggs take to hatch depends upon temperature. Once hatched, the young tadpoles breathe through external gills, which are replaced first by internal gills and then by lungs. The metamorphosis is complete in about three months, and four years later the frogs will breed for the first time.

## Common toad *Bufo bufo*

The life-cycle of the toad is similar to that of the frog, except that the mass movements to the breeding ponds following hibernation take them into deeper water. Also, the males tend to go into the water and croak for a female to join them, whereas frogs simply wait for a female to pass by on the edge of a pond, then jump on her. Male toads seem to be more numerous than the larger females. As a result, there appears to be a continual battle for a mate during the breeding period, which lasts about a fortnight. The female, with the male on her back, swims in search of weeds under the surface of the water. She dives to these and deposits a long string of eggs on the stems and the male fertilises them immediately. The strings may be up to 2m (6½ feet) long and each contains several thousand eggs arranged in groups of twos or threes along it. The duration of the metamorphosis through the tadpole stages to young toads cannot be stated accurately, since it is so dependent upon temperature. The normal range is from two to three months. Males return to the breeding ponds at three years of age, whilst females are usually not mature until they are four.

Toads are notoriously long-lived and some specimens reach fifty years of age. They are most valuable in the garden, where they feed on slugs and other harmful pests. The chances are that the toad in your garden has been working in it longer than you have and you

Common toad.

can repay it for its services by providing a pond and a few plant pots under the shed for use as a summer home and for hibernation.

## Smooth newt *Triturus vulgaris*

Amphibians have evolved from fishy ancestors and still need water for breeding, although the adults breathe atmospheric air through nostrils that lead into primitive lungs. This system is not at all efficient and supplementary respiration is effected through the moist skin which contains a rich supply of blood vessels. Frogs and toads belong to the Salienta order of amphibians (the name derives from the Latin *salire*, to leap), which lack tails and have long legs, whereas newts belong to the order Caudata, from the Latin *cauda*, a tail.

The female smooth newt is dull brown, in contrast to the much brighter male, which even outside the breeding season has a red belly and dense black spotting on his back. Newts tend to be nocturnal and spend the day hidden under stones or garden debris. They are easily overlooked in the garden unless there is a small pond suitable for breeding once they emerge from hibernation in early spring. This can be as early as February after a mild winter. Although only about 10cm (4 inches) long, the male in breeding colours, with his high, wavy crest stretching from head to tail, is a most spectacular creature. The male pursues his female vibrating his crest, displaying his colours and lashing his tail. When she is suitably stimulated, the male sinks to the bottom and drops a pale-coloured packet of sperm from his vent. The female picks this up in her own vent and uses the sperm it contains to fertilise her eggs. The

Smooth newts (male on the left).

Newts breed in their fourth year and, like frogs and toads, can live a long time, if they are not killed by one of their many predators. The increasing number of urban garden ponds may be crucial to the survival of other aquatic organisms in areas where all other suitable breeding sites are polluted or have been filled in. Even ponds of 0·5m (1½ feet) square have proved adequate both for newts and for assorted water beetles, dragonflies, caddis flies and numerous crustaceans. They are also used as bathing pools by birds. It is surprising how many people provide food for winter birds without ever thinking that they need a drink and a bath. One of the most rewarding tasks for an urban naturalist is to keep a diary with a separate section for pond reports and another for events involving visitors to the bird-table.

eggs are laid one at a time over a period of several weeks, each one deposited on a leaf of waterweed and stuck down with adhesive jelly, and she uses her hind legs to wrap each egg in a protective strip of leaf.

Newt tadpoles are even more fish-like than those of toads and frogs. They eat animal matter from the moment they are hatched and do not go through the early vegetarian stage typical of frogs. They also breathe through pink-coloured external gills right up to the change-over to lung breathing. A further contrast with frog tadpoles is seen in the so-called 'balancers'. Newts do not, in fact, use this pair of adhesive anterior appendages, which look rather like antennae, for balancing but for gripping leaves, stones or the sides of a pond or aquarium. In frog and toad tadpoles the hind limbs appear first, but in newts the forelimbs are the first to appear. The precise developmental period depends upon temperature, but eggs laid late in the season may well overwinter in the pond as tadpoles, whilst eggs laid earlier complete their development by the start of the winter and hibernate.

## Bird-tables

There are many books about bird-tables available, but some points need special emphasis. Visitors to your bird-table need protection and a proper diet. To save them from death or injury the table should be made cat-proof by being supported on a stout, slippery pole or fitted with downward-pointing spikes to discourage climbers. Even if you provide bread and nothing else, you will have no difficulty in attracting the bolder birds, such as house sparrows, starlings, pigeons and magpies. This last species is increasing at some would say an alarming rate thanks to our throw-away society. Both the town rubbish tip and the sewage works make an ideal habitat for them, as they are often fringed with tall trees which provide good sites for the domed nests. Both these man-made habitats are full of decaying material which, like the garden compost heap, generates enough heat to guarantee a frost-free feeding area. Even these pickings are not as easy as those from a garden liberally sprinkled with stale bread. Magpies can be seen carrying away huge chunks of bread and returning in a

**Above** Chaffinch.

**Below** Blue tit at nest box.

Song thrush.

remarkably short space of time for more. Like the rest of the intelligent and ingenious crow family, magpies stow away caches of food and remember where they have hidden them.

Magpies also bully their way into the flocks of feeding smaller birds, pinch all the food and eat it at their leisure during the day. For this reason the keen student of bird behaviour needs to provide food for a variety of species. Magpies are seldom agile enough to balance on a bag of nuts and this usually ensures the arrival of blue tits and often great tits and coal tits too. Greenfinches can also prove to be amusingly adventurous, although care should be taken never to make a hungry bird expend too much energy in its often frantic search for food. The welfare of the bird must always be the prime consideration.

It is important to feed birds regularly, preferably at dawn and dusk, since most of their energy is expended at night in holding the body temperature steady. All animals have a built-in biological clock and birds will turn up and wait at the feeding station a few minutes before the appointed hour. You will only appreciate what good time-keepers they are if you feed them at the same time each day.

### Robin *Erithacus rubecula*

The provision of maggots or mealworms bought from a fishing shop will guarantee the appearance of at least one very friendly robin. It is possible to breed mealworms in a container as small as a biscuit tin. The container is filled with layers of bran and potato or apple peelings. This provides a good breeding and feeding habitat for the mealworm beetle.

In Britain the robin is a resident bird but on the Continent, where winters are a lot colder, they are migrants and large numbers flock into Britain to join our resident birds. Whilst the aggressive little residents strive to retain their winter territories, they are forced to abandon them during the hard, freezing days of winter.

### Other bird-table visitors

Regular visitors are likely to include blackbirds and chaffinches – and if fat-rich foods are provided, a drop in temperature will bring song thrushes and even great spotted woodpeckers, which are surprisingly common in towns. One freezing morning in Chelsea I was watching a couple of house sparrows feeding on a lawn when, quick as a flash, a kestrel arrived, pounced on one unfortunate

bird and carried it off over the garden fence into a car-park where it ate a leisurely breakfast in the shade of an old Triumph Herald.

Goldfinches (*Carduelis carduelis*) are showing a remarkable rise in population due to the laws preventing them being sold as cage birds. Bullfinches (*Pyrrhula pyrrhula*) too are welcome visitors to the bird-table, though they may be less welcome to gardeners since they attack the buds on fruit trees and flowering shrubs. Both species need to be encouraged by the provision of an interesting diet. The goldfinch is a seed-eater and seeds can be collected on visits to the autumn countryside or bought as 'wild bird food'. An interesting project is to take a handful of seeds from the mixture and germinate them in pots. The species can then be identified and planted in the wild corner of your garden to provide the birds with a natural diet.

## Nesting boxes

Few urban gardeners can resist the temptation to set up a nesting box for tits. This is fine so long as it is cat-proof and is sited on a north-facing wall or fence to prevent the hot summer sun from roasting the young birds within.

## Feeding birds

Grated coconut and rice should never be fed to birds of any age. Nor should you feed birds during the summer or the young may not get the natural proteins essential for their proper growth. Also, some foods can choke birds. For example, a peanut can kill a young tit. Maggots, mealworms, small earthworms or caterpillars (common species only) are safe enough, but on balance it is better only to operate a feeding station from October to the end of March.

Even those with only a back yard or patio have room for a bird-table or nesting box, or can grow plants in pots to provide a very effective feeding station.

# 6 Churchyards

## The churchyard

Most of our cities evolved by swallowing up villages and their farms and common land. The villages themselves were originally created by clearing the wild wood and in many cases the only remnant of the old woodlands is the churchyard, which no one dared disturb. The yew trees shading the church and cemetery may, therefore, often be older than the city itself, and it is possible that the wildlife living in some churchyards can trace its ancestry back to the ancient woodlands. There are about 40,000 churchyards in Britain, which represents the equivalent of a huge nature reserve in the middle of some very unlikely areas.

## Yew *Taxus baccata*

The yew has always had something of a sombre reputation and was described by Pliny as 'neither verdant, nor graceful, but gloomy, terrible and sapless'. The seeds are certainly poisonous and even the wood was once thought to taint anything in contact with it, so that no one would drink or eat from vessels made of yew and some folk refused to sleep or eat under its shade. Even the generic name of the plant, *Taxus*, derives from the Latin for poison. No wonder is was thought that yew was planted in churchyards as an emblem of death. Another theory is that yew trees were planted to provide wood for the English longbow which won so many battles in the Middle Ages. Wordsworth, I think, had part of the solution in his verse:

> This solitary tree! A living thing
> Produced too slowly ever to decay;
> Of form and aspect too magnificent
> To be destroyed.

Since the yew lives for up to a thousand years and the seed can germinate within the rotting trunk of the parent, the presence of the tree may well have been an original feature of many churchyards and may even sometimes have served to shelter the masons who built the church.

Although the yew is classified as a conifer, its seeds are not contained within a cone but in pink and pulpy seed cups known as arils. Some yews are male, some female, while

Yew 'berries' or arils.

others have both male and female flowers.
The leaves, bark and seeds contain an alkaloid
poison called taxine, but the pink flesh of the
arils is harmless and is eagerly sought by birds,
including song thrushes, blackbirds and jays.
Several mammals also find them a welcome
addition to their diet. It seems that the seeds
themselves, though poisonous to humans,
are not harmful to birds or to some wild
mammals. Also, those which have passed
through the avian or mammalian digestive
tract seem to germinate more easily than those
which have not been subjected to digestive
enzymes. Birds associated with yews and
other planted conifers, and, therefore, often
found in urban churchyards, include the goldcrest, jay, collared dove and treecreeper.
Typical churchyard mammals are the short-
tailed vole, the long-tailed field mouse (or
wood mouse), the common shrew and the
hedgehog.

**Below** Jays often breed in large churchyards.    **Above** Goldcrest.

## Goldcrest *Regulus regulus*

The high-pitched calls and thin song of this tiny 9cm (3½ inch) member of the warbler family is difficult to hear in the silence of a conifer wood and impossible to pick up over the roar of urban traffic. The presence of this pretty little bird is, therefore, often undetected. The diet of the goldcrest consists mainly of spiders, which it finds on the bark of the trees and in the crevices of the church walls. As it searches, it shows surprising agility.

The breeding season begins in April and at this time the male can be distinguished by his crest, which has flecks of orange in it as well as gold. The nest is suspended beneath the branches of a conifer and the hen incubates the clutch of seven to thirteen eggs for between fourteen and eighteen days. Both parents feed the chicks, which leave the nest within three weeks, so there is ample time for a second brood to be produced.

## Jay *Garrulus glandarius*

Although rightly described as one of our most wary birds and an ever-present resident in ancient oak woods, the jay can exist quite happily in an urban churchyard, where it feeds on earthworms, snails, spiders, small mammals and even small birds and their eggs. In winter jays will eagerly consume scraps such as peas, potatoes and fruit and sometimes visit town gardens. On a foggy Sunday morning in December, close to Manchester's Deansgate, I once watched a jay greedily consuming rotting fruit left over from the Saturday street market.

Many of London's larger cemeteries have a breeding pair of jays, their nest invariably sited in a yew tree. After a spectacular display flight the pair alight on a branch and the male displays his streaked crest and colourful body-feathers to the female. The well hidden nest is constructed of sticks lined with mud and with slender roots and hair, which provide good insulation for the eggs. The clutch size varies from five to seven. The young hatch in about two weeks and three weeks later they have grown to the adult size of 34cm (13¼ inches). Only one brood is raised, but jays are good parents, and as they are now less persecuted than in former years, when their colourful feathers were much in demand by milliners, they are expanding their range.

## Collared dove *Streptopelia decaocto*

Before 1930 this fascinating little dove, measuring only 32cm (12½ inches), was confined to the Balkans. It is coloured a uniform grey but is easily identified by a clearly marked half-collar on the nape – a feature obvious in adults of both sexes, though much less obvious in young birds. Suddenly, for no apparent reason unless some genetic change was involved, collared doves began to spread over Europe and commenced breeding in Britain in 1955. Wherever they can find a supply of grain they stay to breed, and both the trees and ledges of nearby churches provide ideal breeding sites. They have become so successful that the species, which once attracted crowds of birdwatchers, is now regarded as a pest in some areas.

Although they were once thought to be too delicate to cope with the British winter, collared doves have a protracted breeding season and eggs have been found in their twiggy nests in every month of the year. The regular breeding period is from March to September, but up to five clutches of two eggs have been recorded in one year. Both birds share the two-week incubation period and the young, like the rest of the pigeon family, are fed directly from the parent's crop on a liquid very similar to the milk produced by mammals. The breeding population of collared doves is now in excess of 60,000 pairs and the increase is likely to be sustained for some time yet. The secret of this incredible success would seem to be that the collared dove has managed to exploit a niche not used by any other species of pigeon, including the even more populous street pigeon.

Collared dove.

## Short-tailed field vole
*Microtus agrestis*

Although they prefer grassland, a churchyard often has a large enough open space dominated by couch grass to make a satisfactory habitat for short-tailed field voles. These voles eat the roots as well as the shoots of the grass and form an important link in the food chain. The fact that they do not hibernate means that a food supply is available throughout the year which can be utilised not only by owls and kestrels but also by domestic cats, foxes and weasels, all of which thrive around town churches. The short-tailed vole is a greyish-brown rodent but, with its round, blunt, friendly face, looks much more like a hamster than a mouse or a rat.

The breeding peak is usually reached between May and July and litters of between four and six young are produced after a gestation period of twenty-one days. The young weigh 2g at birth and are weaned at sixteen days. The body of a field vole is about 11cm (4½ inches) long, including the head, and the tail adds a further 4cm (1⅗ inches). The females can breed when they are six weeks old, but the voles' life expectancy is very short and even in captivity they do not live longer than seventy-five weeks. In the wild they are unlikely to survive for half that time since they have so many predators. A planned sequence of trapping and retrapping will reveal a high population of voles in almost all churchyards – and also quite large numbers of long-tailed field mice and common shrews.

## Long-tailed field mouse
*Apodemus sylvatica*

Living in complex underground tunnel systems, the long-tailed field mouse or wood mouse is indigenous to Britain and is a good example of an ancient woodland animal found in the 'island' surrounding old churches. A small animal, not moving very far and feeding on leaves, fruit and bark, it can live quite

Short-tailed field voles thrive on churchyard grasses.

happily in what it regards as a substantial wood. Despite spending much of their lives in underground tunnels, wood mice are splendid acrobats and climb up tree trunks and along the most slender branches with great agility, using their long tails to balance their bodies. The body measures between 9 and 10cm (about 4 inches) and the tail can add a further 8cm (3³/₁₀ inches). Wood mice have been known to eat the eggs of small birds and frequently use an old nest as a larder, building up large caches of hawthorn berries, rose hips, acorns, beech nuts and tiny pine cones. This can be essential for their survival in winter when snow covers the ground. Nests under the shelter of the evergreen foliage of rhododendrons can be particularly valuable at these times. Wood mice also eat the pupae of butterflies and moths. Nor do their activities slow down in winter – indeed, the animals continue to grow through the cold season. As

with the vole, the life expectancy of the wood mouse is short, but in captivity they have been known to live almost two years.

Large populations of these mice are maintained by their high reproductive efficiency. In summer the nurseries, which are blind endings to branches of the tunnel systems lined with grass, are kept busy. Females can conceive at any time from March onwards, but the peak period for births is July and August and the population is at its maximum in September and October. Five young are born after a gestation period of twenty-five days and they are weaned at twenty-one days, by which time the female is already well advanced on her next pregnancy. Females mature very quickly during the summer and may be pregnant themselves by the time they are six weeks old.

## Common shrew *Sorex araneus*

For its size – the body measures 8cm (3¹/₄ inches), plus a 4cm (1³/₅ inch) tail – the shrew is arguably the fiercest predator found in

Above Long-tailed field mouse, also known as the wood mouse.

Left A young common shrew.

nature. It is so active that its demand for food, mainly earthworms and beetles, seems insatiable. This is because the surface area of the animal is great compared with its average weight of about 12g, which means that it tends to lose body heat to the environment very rapidly and needs lots of food to make up for this heat loss. An examination of the teeth of shrews, which are often found in owl pellets, shows them to be lined with red – the

site of 'poison' glands. These produce a fluid which contains both an anti-coagulant and a tranquilliser that assist the shrew in overcoming its prey.

Shrews live in the leaf litter and can make quite extensive runs under the debris, as well as taking over the underground tunnels of other species, including those of wood mice. The high-pitched squeaking often described as shrewish 'bad temper' is believed to be a method of echo location, rather like that used by bats to find their way around in the dark. The long, pointed snout and sensitive whiskers called vibrissae may also be part of this system.

The breeding period of the common shrew often begins as early as late March and in mild autumns can continue until November, during which time several litters of between five and eight young are produced after a gestation period lasting just over a fortnight. The precise period has not yet been established, as shrews are difficult animals to keep in captivity and are equally difficult to observe in the field – yet another example of the vast gaps which still exist in our knowledge of our native natural history. The female gives birth to her tiny young, each weighing less than 0·5g, in a ball of grass. They develop very slowly and the eyes do not open until about the twentieth day. Even allowing for this slow development, each female can produce up to five litters in a breeding season. The lifespan is very short and it seems unlikely that shrews ever survive beyond their second autumn. There is a large adult mortality during the summer, when the old animals from the previous year are dying off and are replaced by their maturing offspring.

## Pygmy shrew *Sorex minutus*

Most of our churchyards also support a population of pygmy shrews, although this species prefers more open habitats. In Ireland this, the smallest of our mammals, is the only shrew, since the common shrew is not found there. At 5·5cm (2⅕ inches) in length plus a 4cm (1⅗ inch) tail, the pygmy is smaller than the common shrew. Another difference is that it is usually only active during the day, although it needs frequent rests, while common shrew wanders along its burrows over a twenty-four hour period, and its ten spurts of activity are interspersed with a similar number of rest periods.

The breeding season of the pygmy shrew peaks in June and usually only two litters of between three and eight young are produced following a gestation period of about three weeks. The female feeds the young for about the same period. Lactating females require one and a half times their own body weight in food daily. At other times three-quarters of the body weight is required to maintain the basic metabolic rate.

The flesh of shrews is apparently bitter to the taste and although cats occasionally kill them, they seldom eat them. Their main predators are, therefore, birds of prey, especially owls, which seem to locate them by the sounds made as they move through the leaf litter.

## Hedgehog *Erinaceus europaeus*

I have met a great number of urban gardeners who have told me proudly that they have their own toad and hedgehog. Whilst it is true that they may well have their own toad, the hedgehog is much more mobile and, although it may well have a regular route, it usually calls at several feeding stations. If you want to be included on the tour, do not limit the menu to bread and milk. Minced meat, liver and meaty chunks of dog food or dog biscuits will be greedily snapped up, though fish-based cat foods should not be offered.

In nature hedgehogs are important in the control of slugs and do more good in a garden than slug pellets. Although hedgehogs are notoriously resistant to poisons, slug pellets can harm them and if you have a local hedgehog you might try relying on him rather than on poisons. If your garden is close to the local church you will almost certainly have a hedgehog – for a churchyard makes the perfect habitat, providing many feeding niches as well as a large number of suitable spots in which hedgehogs can hibernate.

The natural diet of the hedgehog consists of beetles, caterpillars, earthworms and even birds' eggs. In their search for food hedgehogs often get themselves into potentially lethal situations. Their tendency to fall into cattle grids has been well documented. They also often struggle through drainage gratings and die there, as they are unable to negotiate the steep sides and escape. I have found that a stout net on a long pole can be used to raise hedgehogs to safety. Even in autumn, when it looks as if they have found a good place to hibernate, hedgehogs should be lifted out of

**Above** Hedgehog swimming.

**Below** Hedgehog crossing road.

Swifts are common in most towns and cities.

To prevent the blood clotting an anti-coagulant is produced and extra white blood cells accumulate around the gut to deal with any dangerous build-up of bacteria produced by undigested and rotting food. During periods of extremely cold weather, which would cause the slow-moving blood to freeze, the hedgehog wakes up, has a good shiver to generate heat and goes off in search of food to make good its losses and to find a warmer spot to continue its hibernation.

The two sexes look almost identical, though the males tend to be slightly larger, with an average length of about 25cm (10 inches), plus another 2·5cm (1 inch) for the tail. The most unusual feature of the animal is the layer of spines on the back,. which are in fact modified hairs, each around 2·5cm (1 inch) long. They are provided with powerful knob-like muscles at the base which, when danger threatens, erect the spines to produce a formidable battery. Hedgehogs can probably live for up to ten years, and they are sexually mature when they emerge from their first hibernation. When they mate, after a long period of foreplay the female accepts the advances of the male. The problem of her spines is overcome by the male having a long penis. Also, the female flattens her spines so that the male can mount her. The gestation period is about thirty-two days and the litter of about five soft-spined young is born in a domed nest made of dried grass and leaves. The young are fed by the female for about a month, the male playing no part in looking after his offspring. Great care is needed if a hedgehog's nest is discovered, for although the female may pick up her young and remove them one by one to a safer place she is just as likely to eat them. Some females are able to raise a second litter during the season and it is these autumn youngsters which may have difficulty in reaching the essential weight for survival through the winter.

I know one old lady who visits her churchyard every day to feed the birds, but she never

gratings because they would almost certainly drown during the first flash flood after the start of hibernation. Hedgehogs can, in fact, swim and I once watched one crossing the River Trent in Nottingham with no trouble at all.

Before hibernation the hedgehog builds up its body fat by feeding greedily and it has been shown that individuals weighing under 450g (about 1lb) at the start of this period are unlikely to survive. Hibernation is a most complicated event, involving the reduction of heart-rate, blood pressure and respiration rate.

fails to leave a morsel for her 'urchins' and she knows from many years' experience that each individual has its own territory and a good homing instinct. As already mentioned, like badgers each hedgehog has its own well-trodden foraging route. With careful watching these routes can be mapped and the animal's timetable predicted with some confidence. Although large numbers are killed on the roads, many hedgehogs have evolved a safe nocturnal route and the churchyard dwellers seldom need to move far outside this ideal habitat.

## The church building

Church buildings themselves serve as artificial cliffs and have been eagerly adopted by such species as swifts (surprisingly common even in busy towns), house martins, jackdaws and

Nutcracker.

occasionally barn owls. Peregrines nested on Salisbury Cathedral until the 1950s and the only reliable breeding record for white storks in Britain was on St Giles's Cathedral, Edinburgh, way back in 1416. The black kite, so much a feature of medieval Britain with its filthy streets full of carrion, has now gone, but the churchyard ornithologist may still be rewarded by rarities such as waxwings, crossbills, siskins, linnets, spotted flycatchers and even a nutcracker, a very rare visitor to Britain. The church building is also likely to provide a suitable niche for bats, especially the pipistrelle and the long-eared bat.

### Nutcracker *Nucifraga caryocatactes*

The nutcracker belongs to the crow family and shows irruptive behaviour similar to that of the waxwing when its food, which consists of conifer seeds, nuts and berries, is in short supply. It is easily recognised by its dark

brown plumage speckled with white, which makes it look like an overgrown starling. It is about 31cm (12½ inches) long. Although irruptions are few and far between, there were major autumn and winter invasions in 1968 and again in 1983–4. During February 1984 I watched a flock of eight birds on the church tower at Whalley in Lancashire, not far from the city of Blackburn.

## Swift *Apus apus*

During the hot spring of the same year I was waiting in a long traffic jam in north London close to Archway and wound my window down to let some air into the car. Even above the roar of the traffic I could clearly hear the shriek of a group of swifts, and as the traffic crawled past Highgate cemetery great numbers of these black 'devil birds', as they were once called, with their swept-back wings were darting and swooping overhead. Swifts have been city birds since the days when horses dragged their loads and deposited their dung, thus attracting flies which provided ample food for these summer visitors. Today the fruit markets and the ever increasing number of take-away food shops and restaurants ensure waste bins that are ideal breeding sites for flies, so the swifts stay to breed in high buildings – which differ little from their traditional cliff nest sites. There is every reason to suppose that the swift population has risen along with the number of tall buildings and, except in the days of heavy atmospheric pollution, they have suffered few set-backs. As a result, there are almost certainly more swifts soaring above city centres in the 1980s than was the case a hundred years ago.

Swifts arrive from South Africa during the early days of May and, after raising a single brood of two or three chicks, the majority have left Britain by the end of August. They belong to the order Apodiformes and are closely related to humming birds, although they show a superficial resemblance to swallows. The body is a dusky brown, apart from a whitish throat, the wings are long and scythe-shaped and the tail is not obviously forked as in the swallow tribe. The swift is one of the most aerial of birds, even mating on the wing. Their legs are so short and their wings so long that once on the ground they are unable to take off, which is why high buildings are so important for nesting sites.

The nest sites have usually been selected by the end of May. The nests themselves, which are built in colonies, are constructed of straw glued together with saliva. (In the Orient the nest of a member of the swift family is used to make bird's nest soup.) The eggs are white in colour and are incubated by both sexes for about twenty days, but the fledging period is much more variable and very much depends on the weather. When cold, wet conditions prevail in Britain in June or July, the lack of flying insects drives the parents to fly south and desert their young. The swiftlets do not die but reduce their body temperature, pulse and respiration rate, just as hedgehogs and bats do when preparing for hibernation. This suspended animation is really an example of swiftlets being able to 'hibernate' for a short period should the need arise. The adults eventually return and as temperatures rise the chicks wake up and continue their development.

The swift is much more able to handle urban conditions than either the swallow or the house martin, although the latter, providing atmospheric pollution is not too bad, seems to venture closer to the city centre than the swallow.

## House martin *Delichon urbica*

With its prominent white rump and short forked tail the 12·5cm (5 inch) house martin is easily recognised. As a breeding species it disappeared from inner London between 1890 and 1900, unable to cope any longer with the filthy air. Following the Clean Air Acts of the 1950s they returned to the inner city and their

House martin.

mud nests under the eaves of houses and churches could once again be seen in the capital. The increase has not, however, been as dramatic as expected and it has been suggested that a shortage of mud in the concrete jungle may be responsible. This factor may also have affected the return of the swallow, but the house martin has shown a greater willingness to use nesting boxes. Another factor favouring house martins in city centres is that their short tail means that they are not so manoeuvrable as swallows and consequently hunt for food at higher altitudes. Swallows, twisting and turning at lower levels, come in contact with traffic and other human obstructions and therefore find it more difficult to cope with urban life.

House martins tend to nest in colonies. The nest is a cup of mud built by both sexes and lined with feathers; the clutch of white eggs, usually four or five, is laid from the end of May. Both sexes incubate for fourteen days and the young fly after about three weeks in the nest. Two or occasionally three broods are raised before the birds leave for their South African wintering grounds in September, though the stragglers sometimes leave as late as the end of November. The peak return period is May, but a few hardy individuals arrive as early as the beginning of April.

## Jackdaw *Corvus monedula*

Jackdaws normally nest in cliffs and quarries, though the odd pair find a hollow tree quite acceptable. A church tower and its surrounding trees, therefore, provide a suitable alternative habitat. Apart from Kensington Gardens, central London has not proved popular with jackdaws, but many other city centres have their resident 'daws' and suburbs, including London's, are well populated. As well as churches, the chimney pots of houses

Jackdaw, with young.

have proved increasingly popular breeding sites. Jackdaws are about 32·5cm (13 inches) long and can be distinguished from other members of the crow family by the grey neck and ear coverts of the adult and by the blue ring around the iris of the eye.

Their preference for breeding in colonies makes church towers an ideal site and if there is a nearby rubbish dump where they can scavenge for scraps, young mice, slugs, snails and even vegetables, so much the better. They can be something of a menace to small birds as they love to supplement their diet with a meal of eggs. The nest is built of twigs and lined with fur or grass. The clutch size can be as small as two but is more likely to be from four to six. The female probably incubates these on her own for about eighteen days, but then the male takes his full share of tending and feeding

the young until they can fly at around thirty-three days. Only one breed is usual, although if disaster strikes before the clutch is complete a second set of eggs may be laid. There is some evidence to suggest that the jackdaw population as a whole is increasing and that the species is gradually returning to urban centres. It is a great pity that the same cannot be said for the white barn owl, which is only just holding on to its status as an urban bird.

## Barn owl *Tyto alba*

Although very uncommon these days, the barn owl still breeds in some town parks and churchyards. At the beginning of this present century the barn owl was much more common in central London than the tawny owl. For some reason it suddenly became unpopular and church authorities began to cover up their belfries with netting to prevent nesting. This short-sighted attitude as well as the

Barn owls thrive in old churches and control the mice within.

rebuilding after the blitz of the 1940s, which destroyed old buildings, and the advent of pesticides reduced the population of the barn owl dramatically. What a pity if cities do not manage to woo back this lovely creature, with its white heart-shaped facial disc, lovely golden back and white frontal parts. If church authorities are reluctant to remove the wire netting, they would be amply rewarded if they were to provide nesting boxes – for the barn owl is better than any cat when it comes to removing unwanted rodents.

## Urban bats

There are eighteen species of bat on the British list, which means that out of a total of sixty-eight mammals more than a quarter are chiropterans (the meaning of Chiroptera is 'handwings', a perfect name for a wonderfully evolved group of mammals). All British bats are insect-eaters and catch nocturnal prey, particularly moths, on the wing. The method of hunting is described in Chapter 4. Experts are now able to recognise the electronic impulses of the various species and use bat-detectors to identify and count them.

The populations of all our bats, even the common species, have declined alarmingly in recent years, possibly to some degree as a result of climatic changes, but mainly because of atmospheric pollution, pesticides and loss of habitat. As a result, protection for bats became essential, since originally they occupied woodlands and river valleys, roosting and hibernating in hollow trees and caves, and now that we have destroyed so much of this habitat, species such as the pipistrelle and the long-eared bat have adapted to living in buildings. Although many people have a

Long-eared bat.

horror of bats, most were pleased when, in 1982, bats were eventually given protection and penalties were imposed on those disturbing them. There were, however, a few dissenters and many clergymen expressed fears that bats could ruin their altar covers. Clearly naturalists need to persuade a percentage of the clergy that bats are not as evil as they are painted, that their droppings do not contain bacteria (indeed they are positively beneficial, since they help to insulate lofts) and that the pipistrelle and long-eared bat need all the protection that they can get. Perhaps local naturalists should take up the gauntlet thrown down by the clergy and offer to give advice regarding the natural history problems of ecclesiastical premises.

## Long-eared bat *Plecotus auritus*

The long-eared bat is widely distributed throughout Britain, apart from northern Scotland, and is frequently found roosting in urban buildings, especially old halls and churches. The head and body measure 5cm (2 inches), with the tail adding an extra 4·5cm (1¾ inches). It can also be distinguished from the more common pipistrelle by the very long ears from which it derives its name. Because of their entirely undeserved reputation, bats are often under-recorded in Britain and a regular survey of our church-dwelling chiropterans is undoubtedly needed. There are, in fact, many more dangerous threads to the fabric of our churches than bats, amongst which must be reckoned the timber eating beetles, especially the death watch and the furniture beetle.

# Death watch beetle

*Xestobium rufovillosum*

Originally an inhabitant of woodland where a continual supply of rotting timber was assured, the death watch beetle was carried into buildings with the beams used in their construction and now presents a much greater threat to the fabric of buildings such as churches than bats do. The adult beetle only measures about 0·75cm (³/₁₀ inch), is brown in colour and is occasionally covered with yellowish hairs. Mating occurs during the early spring and the female can produce as many as seventy eggs, which she lays in old timber affected by fungus. The larvae hatch within a period of two weeks to two months, the precise time depending on temperature and moisture – and also, apparently, on the availability of fungus. During the two or three years before it pupates the larva feeds on wood, making damaging inroads into beams. On emergence from the pupa the adults, presumably in order to attract a mate, make the knocking sound which has given the beetle its name. It is especially fond of oak timber, which makes it a particular menace in many city churches, although the adults do not fly very efficiently and, therefore, do not spread quickly from building to building. If the proper protective chemicals are used to treat building materials infestations can be prevented.

# Furniture beetle (woodworm)

*Anobium punctatum*

The adult beetles of this species are extremely mobile and can do serious damage to buildings and furniture. It has been estimated that 75 per cent of all buildings have woodworm in some of the woodwork. To check whether it is present, search for the exit holes by which the adults escape after pupation. These are about 1mm (¹/₂₅ inch) in diameter, whereas those of the death watch beetle are approximately 3mm (³/₂₅ inch). The adult furniture beetle can be recognised by its brown dorsal surface marked with darker lines, its six legs and its prominent antennae.

# Churchyard plants

Finally, it may interest the reader to reflect on the fact that many of our churches were once part of monasteries or were founded by the Knights Hospitallers, who not only tended the spiritual needs of their flock but also provided a medieval health service. Both the monks and the Knights Hospitallers cultivated herbs and many cities once had apothecaries' gardens – indeed, a few remain even today. Some of the plants still found in churchyards were originally planted in these gardens for their medicinal properties. Lesser celandine, for example, was once used in the treatment of piles, yarrow for headaches, dog's mercury for stomach complaints and dandelion for kidney problems. Daisy and eyebright were mixed together to produce an eye lotion and herb Robert was used to treat disorders of the blood. A fascinating project for naturalists is to visit town churchyards, make a list of the plants growing there and look up their uses in herbal medicine. Such research will give you an idea of the role the church played in medicine in the Middle Ages and also of the exent to which the old woodland knowledge has been lost to the modern town dweller.

# Conclusion

It has been the aim of this book to show the variety of wildlife that exists in our towns and cities in spite of pollution and despite our efforts to eliminate the less attractive and the more harmful plants. Much unnecessary damage is done to urban wildlife and much greater awareness of the importance of conservation measures is needed. But no one who sees how hard nature can fight and how resilient it is, can be anything but optimistic about the ability of an impressive number of species to survive and thrive in towns.

Milfoil or yarrow can be white or a delightful pink.

Dog's mercury was once unwisely used as a purgative.

**Opposite** Navelwort was once used to cure stomach-ache in the belief that the navel-like depression in the leaves was a sign of its healing value.

# Further reading

Baines, Chris, *How to Make a Wildlife Garden* (Elm Tree Books, 1985).
Beirne, B. P., *British Pyralid and Plume Moths* (Warne, 1954).
Berrisford, Judith, *The Wild Garden* (Faber, 1973).
Bishop, O. N., *Natural Communities* (John Murray, 1973).
Blackman, R., *Aphids* (Ginn, 1974).
Brink, F. H. vanden, *A Field Guide to the Mammals of Britain and Europe* (Collins, 1967).
Bristow, W. S., *The World of Spiders* (Collins, 1958).
Burton, J., *The Oxford Book of Insects* (OUP, 1968).
Chinery, M., *A Field Guide to the Insects of Britain and Northern Europe* (Collins, 1973).
Chinery, M., *The Natural History of the Garden* (Collins, 1977).
Clegg, John, *The Freshwater Life of the British Isles* (Warne, 1965).
Clegg, John, *The Observer's Book of Pond Life* (Warne, 1974).
Cloudsley-Thompson, J. L., *Spiders, Scorpions, Centipedes and Mice* (Pergamon, 1968).
Colyer, C. N., and Hammond, C. O., *Flies of the British Isles* (Warne, 1951).
Eason, E. H., *Centipedes of the British Isles* (Warne, 1964).
Engelhardt, W., *The Young Specialist Looks at Pond Life* (Burke, 1968).
Evesham, B., and Jackson, N., *Slugs: A Key for Amateurs and Professionals* (*Country-Side*, Spring 1982).
Fitter, R. S. R., *London's Natural History* (Collins, 1945).
Flegg, J. J. M., and Glue, D. E., *Nestboxes* (British Trust for Ornithology, 1972).
Freethy, Ron, *The Making of the British Countryside* (David & Charles, 1981).
Freethy, Ron, *How Birds Work* (Blandford, 1982).
Freethy, Ron, *Man and Beast – the Natural and Unnatural History of British Mammals* (Blandford, 1983).
Freethy, Ron, *British Birds in their Habitats* (Crowood Press, 1985).
Freethy, Ron, *The River Mersey* (Terence Dalton, 1985).
Glue, David, *Collecting and analysing bird pellets* (RSPB booklet).
Harrison, J., and Grant, P., *The Thames Transformed* (Deutsch, 1976).
Hartley, P. H. T., *The Bird Garden* (RSPB, 1957).
Hatfield, A. H., *How to Enjoy Your Weeds* (Muller, 1969).
Heath, J., Pollard, E., and Thomas, J. A., *Atlas of Butterflies in Britain and Ireland* (Viking, 1984).
Howart, T. G., *Colour Identification Guide to Butterflies of the British Isles* (Viking, 1984).
Hubbard, C. E., *Grasses* (Penguin, 1954).
Janus, H., *The Young Specialist Looks at Molluscs* (Burke, 1965).
Linssen, E. F., *Beetles of the British Isles* (2 vols) (Warne, 1959).
Mabey, R., *Food for Free* (Collins, 1972).
Macan, T. T., *Freshwater Ecology* (Longman, 1966).
Mason, C. F. F., *Biology of Freshwater Pollution* (Longman, 1981).
Mellanby, H., *Animal Life in Freshwater* (Methuen, 1948).
Miles, P. M., and Miles, H. B., *Freshwater Ecology* (Hulton, 1969).
Murton, R. K., *Man and Birds* (Collins, 1971).
Nichols, D., Cooke, J., and Whiteley, D., *The Oxford Book of Invertebrates* (OUP, 1971).
Nicholson, E. M., *Birds and Men* (Collins, 1951).
Nixon, M., and Whiteley, D., *The Oxford Book of Vertebrates* (OUP, 1972).

Ragge, D. R., *Grasshoppers, Crickets and Cockroaches* (Warne, 1965).
Russel, Sir E. J., *The World of the Soil* (Collins, 1957).
Salisbury, Sir Edward, *Weeds and Aliens* (Collins, 1961).
Soper, T., *The New Bird Table Book* (David & Charles, 1973).
Soper, T., *Wildlife Begins at Home* (David & Charles, 1975).
Savory, T. H., *The Spider's Web* (Warne, 1952).
Savory, T. H., *The World of Small Animals* (University of London Press, 1955).
Skinner, B., *Colour Identification Guide to Moths of the British Isles* (Viking, 1984).
South, R., *The Moths of the British Isles* (2 vols) (Warne, 1961).
Spradbery, J. P., *Wasps* (Sidgwick & Jackson, 1973).
Step, E., *Bees, Wasps, Ants and Allied Insects of the British Isles* (Warne, 1932).
Stokoe, E. J., *The Caterpillars of the British Moths* (Series I and II) (Warne, 1948).
Sutton, S. L., *Woodlice* (Ginn, 1972).
Tweedie, M., *Insect Life* (Collins, 1977).
Wheeler, A., *The Tidal Thames* (Routledge & Kegan Paul, 1979).
Willoughby, L. G., *Freshwater Biology* (Hutchinson, 1981).
Wilson, Ron, *The Urban Dweller's Wildlife Companion* (Blandford, 1983).

**British Naturalists' Association Guides**
Other titles already published in this series (all available from The Crowood Press) are:
*Ponds and Streams* by John Clegg (1985)
*Fields, Farms and Hedgerows* by Brian Lee (1985)
*Woodlands* by John Cloudsley-Thompson (1985)
*Mountain and Moorland* by Brian Brookes (1985)
*Coast and Shore* by Brian Barnes (1986).

# Acknowledgements

During the preparation of this book for publication I received help from many people. In particular, I would like to thank the photographers listed below; Carole Pugh, who produced the excellent line drawings; and Brian Lee, who read the text with meticulous care. To my wife, Marlene, I extend my special thanks for typing the manuscript during a very difficult period.

# Picture credits

## Colour and Black & White Photos

Richard Abernethey: *page* 11 (top)
Will Bown: *pages* 8, 34 (both), 42, 66 (bottom), 114
P. S. Cameron: *page* 72
Michael Chesworth: *pages* 28, 77, 111 (top)
Michael Clark: *page* 120
John Clegg: *pages* 15 (bottom), 17, 18 (all), 22, 50 (top), 60, 71, 102
J. L. Cloudsley-Thompson: *page* 56 (bottom)
Michael Edwards: frontispiece, *pages* 9 (top), 12, 15 (top left and right), 26 (bottom), 35, 39, 43, 44 (top), 51 (top), 53, 54 (top right and left), 63, 64 (both), 66 (top), 68, 75, 81 (top and bottom), 82 (bottom), 84, 88, 90 (both), 95, 97 (bottom), 98 (both), 106, 113 (both)
Ron Freethy: *pages* 10, 23 (top), 51 (bottom), 73, 122 (both), 123
John Heap: *page* 78 (top)
Alan W. Heath: *pages* 16, 41, 56 (top and middle), 81 (middle), 111 (bottom)
Eric and David Hosking: *pages* 13, 14, 21, 23 (bottom), 30, 62, 74, 107 (top), 118
Robert Howe: *pages* 78 (bottom), 82 (top), 87 (left), 96, 97 (top), 101, 103 (top), 104, 110
George E. Hyde: *page* 89 (both)
Trevor James: *page* 99
Frank Lane Picture Agency/Arthur Christiansen: *page* 115
Brian Lee: *pages* 19 (top), 54 (bottom), 55, 107 (bottom)
Charles Linford: *pages* 76, 85
Newcastle University Botany Department: page 67
Barry Ogden: *pages* 19 (bottom), 50 (bottom), 58, 59, 79, 87 (right), 103 (bottom)
Brian Oldfield: *pages* 26 (top), 38
Bill Wilkinson: *page* 25

## Cover Photos

Top left: Michael Edwards
Top right: Robert Howe
Bottom left: Michael Edwards
Bottom right: Robert Howe

## Line Drawings

The line illustrations are by Carole Pugh.

# Index

*Note:* bold numerals denote page numbers of illustrations.

albinism 40, **42**, 83, **84**
annual seablite *Suaeda maritima* 67
aphids 57
ants 55–7, **56, 57**
*Argulus* fish louse 81, **81**
*Asellus* 19, **19**, 20

badger *Meles meles* **9**, 10
bats 119–20
bearded tit *Panurus biarmicus* 30
beetles 59
biological oxygen demand (BOD) 16, 17
birch *Betula* spp 73
bird pellets 39–40, **41**
bird-tables 102–105
bittern *Botaurus stellaris* 30
black ant *Lasius niger* 55
blackbird *Turdus merula* 10, **39**, **42**, 90, 105
blackflies *Simulium* spp 16–17
black redstart *Phoenicurus ochruros* 61, 62, **62**
black throated diver *Gavia arctica* 30
black slug *Limax cinereoniger* 94
bluebottle *Calliphora vomitoria* 47
blue tit *Parus caeruleus* **103**, 105
bracket fungus 73
brandlings *Eisenia foetida* 40
*Buddleia davidii* 96
bullfinch *Pyrrhula pyrrhula* 105
butterbur *Petasites hybridus* 22, **23**

cabbage white butterfly 78, 80
caddis flies 17, **17, 18**
Canada goose 85
Canadian pondweed *Elodea canadensis* 22, **22**
cats, feral **35**, 36–8
chaffinch *Fringilla coelebs* **103**, 105
*Chironomus* midges 13, 20
choice chamber 58, 61
cockroaches 43, 45–7
collared dove *Streptopelia decaocto* 107, 108, **109**
coot *Fulica atra* **82**, 84–5
cotoneaster 94–5

couch grass *Agropyron* 80
*Cryptococcus neoformans* 43
cuckoo pint *Arum maculatum* 10, **12**, 21
*Cyclops* 81

dabchick *see* little grebe
daisy *Bellis perennis* 10, 21, 68, 100, 121
dandelion *Taraxacum officinale* 10, 21, 68, 80, 100, 121
*Daphnia* 81, **81**
death watch beetle *Xestobium rufovillosum* 121
dog's mercury *Mercurialis perennis* 10, 121, **122**
dunnock *Prunella modularis* 10, 70, 90

earthworms 40, 90, **91**, 92, 105
elephant hawk moth *Deilephila elpenor* 52, 53, **54**
*Eristalis* rat-tailed maggot 20
Essex skipper *Thymelicus lineola* 30
eyebright 121

feral pigeon 42–3
ferns 49, 52
firethorn *Pyracantha coccinea* 95
flatworms 18, **18**
fowl pest 43
fox *Vulpes vulpes* **9**, 10
foxtails *Alopecurus* 80
freshwater shrimp *Gammarus pulex* 15–16, **16**
frog, common *Rana temporaria* 29, **29, 99**, 100
furniture beetle *Anobium punctatum* 121

garden slug *Arion hortensis* 94
garden snail *Helix aspersa* 48, 93
garden tiger moth **90**
glaucus gull *Larus hyperboreus* 30
goat's rue *Galega officinalis* 31
goldcrest *Regulus regulus* 107, 108
goldeneye *Bucephala clangula* 24
goldfinch *Carduelis carduelis* 105
gravel pits 27–8

great crested grebe *Podiceps cristatus* **26**, 28–9
great northern diver *Gavia immer* 30
great spotted woodpecker *Dendrocopos major* 73, **74**
green-veined white butterfly *Pieris napi* **78**, 80
grey squirrel *Sciurus carolinensis* **77**, 79–80
grey slug *Limax maximus* 94
groundsel *Senecio vulgaris* 65
gypsywort *Lycopus europaeus* 22
*Gyrinus* 81

hart's tongue fern *Phyllitis scolopendrium* 52
harvest mouse *Micromys minutus* 28
hawkbit *Leontodon* spp 80
hawthorn 80, 90
hedgehog *Erinaceous europaeus* 112, **113**, 114–5
herb Robert *Geranium robertianum* 53, **54**, 68, 121
heron *Ardea cinerea* **30**
Himalayan balsam *Impatiens glandulifera* 22
hoopoe *Upupa epops* **8**, 10
housefly *Musca domestica* 47
house martin *Delichon urbica* 115, 116–17, **117**
house mouse *Mus musculus* **34**, 35–6
house sparrow *Passer domesticus* 40, 105

ice plant *Sedum spectabile* 96
Ichneumons **87**, 87–9, 90
industrial melanism 70–1
ivy leaved toadflax *Cymbalaria muralis* 53, **55**

jackdaw *Corvus monedula* 115, 117–18, **118**
jay *Garrulus glandarius* **107**, 108

kestrel *Falco tinnunculus* 10, 38, **38**, **41**, 105
kingfisher *Alcedo atthis* 25, **26**

ladybird *Coccinella septempunctata* **58**, 59
lady's smock *Cardamine pratensis* 80
lapwing *Vanellus vanellus* **64**, 65
lead poisoning in wildfowl 24–5
leeches *Glossiphonia* spp 14–15, **15**
*Lepraria incana* 49
lesser celandine 121
lichens 48–9, **50**
little grebe *Podiceps ruficollis* 85, **85**
little ringed plover *Charadrius dubius* 61, **63**, 63–4
liverworts 49
long-eared bat *Plecotus auritus* 115, 120, **120**
long-tailed field mouse *Apodemus sylvatica* 107, 109–10, **111**

magpie *Pica pica* 102, 104
magpie moth *Abraxas grossulariata* 89, **89**, **90**
maidenhair spleenwort *Asplenium trichomanes* 49, **51**, 52
mallard *Anas platyrhynchos* 24
Manchester ship canal 25
marjoram *Origanum vulgare* 96
mayfly larva 14, **15**
mistle thrush *Turdus viscivorus* 10, **11**
molluscs 93–4
monkey flower *Mimulus guttatus* 22
moorhen *Gallinula chloropus* **82**, 83–4, **84**, 85
mosses 49, **51**
mothing 71–2
mottled beauty moth *Cleora repandata* 71
mugwort 21
mute swan *Cygnus olor* 24, **25**
Myriapoda 59

navelwort *Cotyledon umbelicus* 90, **123**
nematodes **91**, 92–3
Newcastle disease, *see* fowl pest
newt, smooth *Triturus vulgaris* 101, **102**
nutcracker *Nucifraga caryocatactes* **115**, 115–16
nut tree tussock moth *Colacasia coryli* 71

*Oniscus asellus* 58
osprey *Pandion haliaetus* 30
owl
  barn *Tyto alba* 76, 115, 118–19, **119**
  little *Athene noctua* 76
  pellets **41**
  tawny *Strix aluco* **75**, 76

oystercatcher *Haematopus ostralegus* 65, **66**

pale cream netted slug *Agriolimax reticulatus* 94
peacock butterfly *Inachis io* 80, 96, 97, **97**, **98**, 99
pectoral sandpiper *Calidris melanotos* 30
peppered moth *Biston betularia* 70–1, **71**
peregrine falcon 115
pied wagtail **21**, 21–2
Pharoah's ant *Monomorium pharaonis* 55
pineapple weed *Matricaria matricarioides* 21, 22, 68, 100
pipistrelle bat *Pipistrellus pipistrellus* 72, 72–3, 115
pitfall trap 57
plane *Platanus* spp 69
*Pleurococcus* 48, **50**
pochard *Aythya ferina* 13, 24
pooter 53
*Porcellio scaber* 58
privet *Ligustrum vulgare* 86
privet hawk moth *Sphinx ligustri* 86–7, **87**, **88**

ragwort *Senecio jacobaea* 10, 21, **64**, 65, 100
ragwort, Oxford *S. squalidus* 65
rat, black *Rattus rattus* 32, **33**
rat, brown *Rattus norvegicus* 33, **34**
red admiral *Vanessa atalanta* **95**, 96–7
red-necked grebe *Podiceps griseigena* 30
rhododendron 69
ringed plover *Charadrius hiaticula* 63
robin *Erithacus rubecula* 10, **43**, 90, 105
Roesel's bush cricket *Metrioptera roeselii* 30
rosebay willowherb *Epilobium angustifolium* 21, 52, **54**
ruddy duck *Oxyura jamaicensis* 30

salmon *Salmo salar* 13, 81
saltmarsh grass *Puccinellia maritima* 66
  reflexed *P. distans* 66, **67**, 68
scalloped hazel moth *Gonodontis bidendata* 71
scurvy grass *Cochlearia officinalis* 67
sea aster *Aster tripolium* **66**, 67
sea barley *Hordeum murinum* 67
sea plantain *Plantago maritima* 67
sea spurreys 67, 68
shelduck *Tadorna tadorna* 13, **14**, 24

shepherd's purse *Capsella bursa-pastoris* 10, 68
shrew
  common *Sorex araneus* 61, 107, 110–11, **111**
  pygmy *Sorex minutus* 112
skullcap Scutellaria galericulata 22
slugs 91, 93
small tortoiseshell *Aglais urticae* 80, 96, **97**, **98**, 99
snails 91, 93
snout moth *Hypena proboscidalis* 89
soapwort *Saponaria officinalis* 12, **19**, 20
song thrush 90, **104**
spiders 60–1
*Squamaria muralis* 49, **50**
starling *Sternus vulgaris* 41–2, **44**
stonefly larva 14, **15**
swift *Apus apus* **114**, 115, 116

teal *Anas crecca* **23**, 24
teasel *Dipsacus fullonum* 12, **19**, 20
three-spined stickleback *Gasterosteus aculeatus* 81, 83
toad *Bufo bufo* 100, **101**
treecreeper *Certhia familiaris* 76, **76**, 107
tubifex worms 13, 19
tufted duck *Aythya fuligala* 13, **13**, 24

vole
  short-tailed field *Microtus agrestis* 28, **38**, 109
  water *Arvicola terrestris* 28, **28**
wall brown butterfly *Lasiommata megera* 80, **81**
wallflower *Cheiranthus cheiri* 53
wall rue *Asplenium ruta-muraria* 49, 52
Walthamstow marshes 29–30
waved umber moth *Hemerophila abruptoria* 71
waxwing *Bombycilla garrulus* 8, 95, 115
white caterpillar
  large *Pieris brassicae* **79**, 80, 96
  small **79**, 96
white stork *Ciconia ciconia* 30
whooper swan 85
wigeon *Anas penelope* 24
willow 21
woodlice 57–8
woodpigeon 11
woolly-bear caterpillar **89**
wren *Troglodytes troglodytes* 90

yarrow 121, **122**
yew *Taxus baccata* **106**, 106–7